W9-ARZ-539

FOUNDATIONS OF MODERN PSYCHOLOGY SERIES
Richard S. Lazarus, *Editor*

THE PSYCHOLOGICAL DEVELOPMENT OF THE CHILD, Paul H. Mussen

TESTS AND MEASUREMENTS, Leona E. Tyler

MOTIVATION AND EMOTION, Edward J. Murray

PERSONALITY AND ADJUSTMENT, Richard S. Lazarus

CLINICAL PSYCHOLOGY, Julian B. Rotter

SENSORY PSYCHOLOGY, Conrad G. Mueller

PERCEPTION, Julian E. Hochberg

LEARNING, Sarnoff A. Mednick

LANGUAGE AND THOUGHT, John B. Carroll

SOCIAL PSYCHOLOGY, William W. Lambert and Wallace E. Lambert

PHYSIOLOGICAL PSYCHOLOGY, Philip Teitelbaum

EDUCATIONAL PSYCHOLOGY, Donald Ross Green

THE NATURE OF PSYCHOLOGICAL INQUIRY, Ray Hyman

ORGANIZATIONAL PSYCHOLOGY, Edgar H. Schein

PHILIP TEITELBAUM

Professor of Psychology and Director of the Physiological Psychology Training Program, University of Pennsylvania; researcher and author of numerous articles on the physiological basis of motivated behavior; consulting editor for the Journal of Comparative and Physiological Psychology; member of the American Physiological Society and International Brain Research Organization (IBRO).

Physiological

Psychology

FUNDAMENTAL PRINCIPLES

PRENTICE-HALL, INC., *Englewood Cliffs, New Jersey*

PHYSIOLOGICAL PSYCHOLOGY: Fundamental Principles, *Philip Teitelbaum*

PRENTICE-HALL FOUNDATIONS
OF MODERN PSYCHOLOGY SERIES
Richard S. Lazarus, *Editor*

Current printing (last digit):
10   9   8   7

PRENTICE-HALL INTERNATIONAL, INC., *London*
PRENTICE-HALL OF AUSTRALIA, PTY., LTD., *Sydney*
PRENTICE-HALL OF CANADA, LTD., *Toronto*
PRENTICE-HALL OF INDIA PRIVATE LIMITED, *New Delhi*
PRENTICE-HALL OF JAPAN, INC., *Tokyo*

Designed by Harry Rinehart
Illustrations by BMA Associates

C

Foundations
of Modern Psychology
Series

The tremendous growth and vitality of psychology and its increasing fusion with the social and biological sciences demand a new approach to teaching at the introductory level. The basic course, geared as it usually is to a single text that tries to skim everything—that sacrifices depth for superficial breadth —is no longer adequate. Psychology has become too diverse for any one man, or a few men, to write about with complete authority. The alternative, a book that ignores many essential areas in order to present more comprehensively and effectively a particular aspect or view of psychology, is also insufficient. For in this solution, many key areas are simply not communicated to the student at all.

The Foundations of Modern Psychology is a new and different approach to the introductory course. The instructor is offered a series of short volumes, each a self-contained book on the special issues, methods, and content of a basic topic by a noted authority who is actively contributing to that particular field. And taken together, the volumes cover the full scope of psychological thought, research, and application.

The result is a series that offers the advantage of tremendous flexibility and scope. The teacher can choose the subjects he wants to emphasize and present them in the order he desires. And without necessarily sacrificing breadth, he can provide the student with a much fuller treatment of individual areas at the introductory level than is normally possible. If he does not have time to include all the volumes in his course, he can recommend the omitted ones as outside reading, thus covering the full range of psychological topics.

Psychologists are becoming increasingly aware of the importance of reaching the introductory student with high-quality, well-written, and stimulating material, material that highlights the continuing and exciting search for new knowledge. The Foundations of Modern Psychology Series is our attempt to place in the hands of instructors the best textbook tools for this purpose.

Contents

Introduction

Human behavior often seems complicated and unpredictable. Its abnormalities can be terrifying because they are so strange, and because we find them impossible to control or to understand. If we could break down complicated behavior into a combination of simple parts that are familiar from past experience, easily identifiable in many situations, and subject to variables we can recognize and manipulate, then we could predict behavior and control it. We would then understand it.

A child trying to understand how a clock works does two things: He takes it apart and puts it back together

1

again. If he can figure out how the gears, ratchets, pinions, and springs combine to produce movement, and if he can put those parts back together so that the clock tells time correctly again, he understands it. These two steps are essentially the approach of physiological psychology to behavior.

First, analyze behavior: break it down into its simple elements. Then synthesize: put the elements back together to reproduce the original behavior. The nervous system is what makes us tick, so we must take it apart. Chop it into smaller chunks and our behavior also decomposes into simple fragments. Integrate the units of the nervous system and you synthesize behavior. To understand behavior, then, we must discover its elements.

Physiological psychology, therefore, is a *method of approach* to the understanding of behavior as well as a *set of principles* that relate the function and organization of the nervous system to the phenomena of behavior.

In this introductory book, I have tried to illustrate, by the use of examples from current scientific work, those principles of method, function, and organization which seem to me to be permanently a part of physiological psychology. The examples may become dated with the passage of time, but the principles should remain useful.

The Method
of Physiological
Psychology

Physiological psychologists apply the experimental method to the study of behavior. Typically, we start with a phenomenon in behavior that we wish to understand. For instance, in Germany during the First World War, it was observed that many soldiers had great difficulty in seeing well at night. Some scientists believed that this night blindness might be caused by a deficient diet, especially one lacking Vitamin A. Since the essence of the scientific method is *comparison*, to find out whether Vita-

3

1

min A helps us to see better at night, we compare the night vision of people eating a diet rich in Vitamin A with that of people eating food deficient in Vitamin A. If all other factors that might affect vision are equal in the two groups, those people eating Vitamin A should see better in the dark than those lacking it. We might wait for such people to happen along, as a physician in an eye clinic might do, but this *method of observation* would clearly not be as direct and as well-controlled as the *experimental method,* in which we create the single relevant difference in the diet by our own manipulation. Therefore, the first step is to *produce the phenomenon experimentally,* preferably in the laboratory, where we can control the conditions. If the treatment is painful or is otherwise impractical for use on human subjects, the physiological psychologist must experiment on animals, making sure, however, that the phenomenon seen in human behavior is also present in the behavior of the animal he has chosen. One can, for example, produce night blindness in rats as well as in human beings by allowing them only a diet deficient in Vitamin A.

THE METHOD OF ANALYSIS: SIMPLIFY TO UNDERSTAND

Not only does the experimental method enable us to produce relevant conditions at will, but it also allows us to use the method of analysis, which is basic to the process of understanding. It was clearly stated by the French philosopher René Descartes in 1628. As used in the experimental method, we can formulate the method of analysis as follows:

In studying any phenomenon, dissect away everything that is not essential to it. In a word, simplify. Then study the simple system that remains, to discover the variables that produce the phenomenon.

The basic assumption is that if the same phenomenon is still present in the simpler system, then it still contains all the variables necessary to produce that phenomenon. Because what has been removed is irrelevant, fewer extraneous influences operate, and the essential elements will be more clearly revealed. We can use the principle of analysis, not only as a way of doing experimental research, but also as a way of seeking understanding by clarifying our thoughts. It is the basic method of physiological psychology.

Let us consider our example of human night vision. To understand a phenomenon, we first describe it accurately. From psychophysics, the branch of psychology devoted to precise measurement of the relation between an external stimulus and our perception of it, we learn that our ability to see in the dark increases the longer we are without light. The absolute threshold (the intensity of white light we can just barely see in darkness) is a measure of our sensitivity to light. The more sensitive the eye of the observer, the lower is the threshold. As one remains in the dark (see Figure 1-1A), the threshold (measured in microlux, a unit of light intensity) can decrease as much as ten thousandfold—that is, from 100,000 to 10 microlux. The process (known as dark-adaptation) is essentially complete after about 45 minutes.

Figure 1-1B shows that people fed a diet deficient in Vitamin A have poor night vision. To be just visible, light must be of much greater intensity

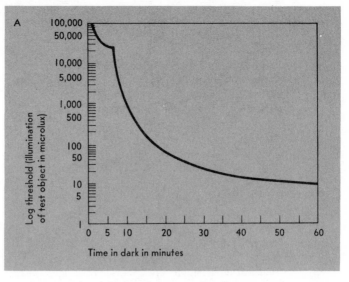

Figure 1-1 (A) Course of dark-adaptation in the human eye. (Dieter's data from Kohlrausch. Handb. norm. path. Physiol., 1931, 1, 394. Replotted by Wright and Granit. Brit. J. Ophthal., 1938, Suppl. 9.) (B) The cure of night-blindness with carotene. Following a standard light-adapta-tion, the measurement of dark-adaptation shows both cone and rod pla-teaus to be above their normal range (indicated by the heavy white hori-zontal lines). After dark-adaptation was completed, 20,000 International Units of carotene in oil were administered in gelatin capsules orally. For 12 to 14 minutes the rod threshold remained constant, then it fell rapidly to normal. Immediate repetition of the standard adaptation procedure showed both cone and rod plateaus to have entered their normal ranges. (G. Wald and D. Steven. Proc. nat. Acad. Sci., 1939, 25, 344–349.)

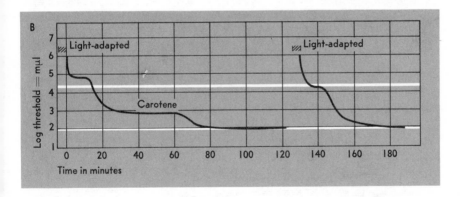

for them than for normal subjects. But feeding them carotene, a form of Vitamin A, restores their ability to see in the dark (Figure 1-1B).

How can we use the method of analysis to understand this phenomenon? Can we simplify the visual system involved in human night vision? When an observer decides that he has seen a light, he uses his entire visual system; the receptors in his retina are stimulated by light and send the information along the optic nerves to visual systems in the brain. A complex process ensues: storage of the information, comparison with past visual experiences, and a decision that the light has been seen. Then, judgment must be voiced before we learn that the subject has indeed seen the light. The simplest part of the system is, of course, the retinal receptor. If we could measure the response

The Method
of
Physiological
Psychology

of a single receptor to light, we could determine whether it grows more sensitive to light the longer it has been in the dark. If so, and if the dark-adaptation curve of a single receptor is identical to that of the judging observer, we can assume that all the variables necessary to produce the phenomenon of dark-adaptation are present in the photochemical and nervous process of stimulation of a receptor by light. If not, then we must include more of the visual system if we wish to study the phenomenon of dark-adaptation.

Exactly this line of reasoning (the method of analysis) was used by H. Keffer Hartline in 1932 to study many phenomena of vision. A few years earlier, in 1926, E. D. Adrian and Yngve Zotterman had succeeded in measuring the electrical activity of a single sensory nerve fiber. This activity contained all the information being transmitted from a stretch receptor in a frog's chest muscle to the rest of the frog's nervous system. Now, Hartline reasoned, if we could stimulate a single visual receptor, or find an animal in which each receptor is connected to its own optic nerve fiber, we could record from a single optic nerve fiber and measure the receptor's response to light. Unfortunately, in most species, retinal receptors are extremely small

Figure 1-2 (A) *Apparatus for stimulating the isolated Limulus eye with light and recording from its attached optic nerve. The eye (E) is mounted on the front wall of a moist chamber (MC) by means of melted paraffin, and the attached optic nerve (N) is slung over two silk threads soaked in sea water which serve as recording electrodes. The whole system is placed in an electrically shielded and thermally insulated box (B) with the front surface of the eye at the focus of a microscope objective (M). A light source sends rays through a slit or a pinhole in diaphragm (D), and the image of this aperture is focused by the objective onto the cornea of the eye. Intensity is controlled by neutral-tint filters (F) and the duration of exposure is regulated by a shutter (S). The moist chamber containing the eye-nerve preparation is mounted on a platform (P) carried by a micrometer manipulator. The manipulator controls (X, Y, Z) outside the dark box enable the light image to be positioned accurately on the eye. The silk electrodes connect at (C) to a vacuum tube amplifier (see Figure 1-2 (B)). (H. K. Hartline and C. H. Graham. J. cell. comp. Physiol., 1932, 1, 277–295.) (B) Simplified diagram of apparatus used in recording potentials in nerves by means of an amplifier and cathode*

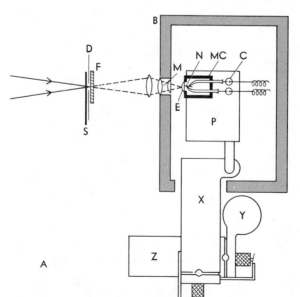

and densely packed. Because of these characteristics and because of the diffraction and scattering of light as it passes through the lens and fluids in the eye, it is difficult to stimulate a single receptor. In addition, in many of the higher animals, many receptors converge in their connections to the cells of the optic nerve, and therefore, when many receptors are stimulated, the activity of a single optic nerve fiber does not represent the activity of a single receptor. For these reasons, Hartline chose to study the eye of the horseshoe crab (*Limulus polyphemus*), where each retinal receptor appeared to be connected only to its own optic nerve fiber.

The experimental set-up used by Hartline demonstrates the principles of many electrophysiological studies of sensory processes. Figure 1-2A shows the eye with its attached optic nerve (consisting of many fibers) dissected away from the crab. The nerve is placed in a chamber which is kept at a constant temperature and is moistened with a sea-water solution. Such a preparation remains physiologically normal for many hours. In the chamber, the nerve lies loosely across two recording electrodes which detect the differences in electrical potential generated by the activity of the nerve fibers. These tiny potential differences (approximately 0.6 millivolts) are fed into an electronic

ray oscilloscope. In the oscilloscope tube an electron source produces an electron beam which is focused on the fluorescent screen and may be viewed or photographed as a spot of light. A potential difference between the two Y plates causes the spot to shift vertically, and between the X plates horizontally. Stimulation triggers the horizontal sweep cam so that the spot, starting from the left of the screen, moves to the right at a certain velocity. When the nerve impulse (I) passes the proximal lead electrode, the amplified action potential causes an upward deflection of the spot which rises to a maximum and then declines. The impulse does not reach the distal electrode since it is on a killed portion of the nerve, so the action potential is monophasic. (Adapted from J. Erlanger and H. S. Gasser. Electrical Signs of Nervous Activity. *Philadelphia: University of Pennsylvania Press, 1937.*)

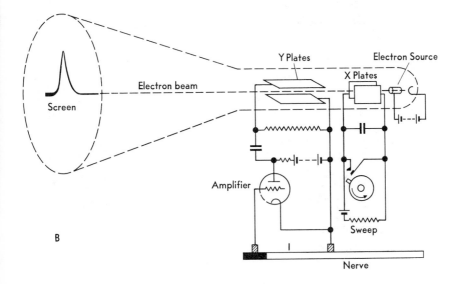

B

amplifier and recorded, either on the face of a cathode-ray tube (oscilloscope) (Figure 1-2B) or on a fast-moving paper sheet (oscillograph). The nerve is dissected with glass needles under a microscope until only a single nerve fiber remains intact. The activity of this fiber should then reflect the excitatory effect of light on the visual receptor to which it is connected.

We are now ready for the experiment. We stimulate the crab eye with a short flash of light, just bright enough to stimulate the receptor. As shown at the bottom of Figure 1-3, after a short pause (the latent period), a burst of three or four electrical impulses (each identical in amplitude) travel along the nerve fiber followed by a steady frequency of about 5 impulses per second. We then increase the intensity of the light flash by a factor of 100. A more rapid burst of nerve impulses now occurs, settling down to a steady frequency of about 20 per second. Thus, the stronger the intensity of the flash, the higher the rate of firing generated along the nerve fiber. But each nerve impulse is identical in amplitude, no matter how strong the stimulus. This result illustrates the all-or-none law of nerve activity demonstrated earlier by Adrian. Therefore, frequency of firing is the only way a single nerve cell can signal

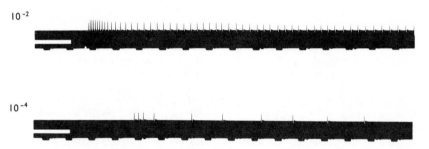

10^{-2}

10^{-4}

Figure 1-3 Discharge of impulses in an optic nerve fiber (eye of Limulus) in response to illumination of the eye at two different intensities (relative values given at left). Eye partially light-adapted. Signal of exposure to light blackens out white line above time marker. Time marked in ⅕ sec. (Adapted from H. K. Hartline. Harvey Lectures, *1941–1942, 37, 39–68.)*

the intensity of a stimulus. In our experiment, if the light is left on, after the initial rapid burst of firing, the rate of firing generated in the nerve fiber decreases within a few seconds to a slower, steady rate. This decrease in the response of a receptor to a maintained stimulus is known as *sensory adaptation.*

If we let the crab eye sit in the dark, we find that the longer it is without light the more sensitive it becomes (see Figure 1-4). Like the human eye, it responds to light previously too weak to stimulate it. Thus, the phenomenon of dark-adaptation is still present in the single optic fiber even when it has been removed from the animal. Therefore, the photochemical and nervous processes that generate optic nerve activity in response to light are sufficient to produce dark-adaptation. More complex processes of perception, judgment, and behavioral response are irrelevant. By the method of analysis, therefore,

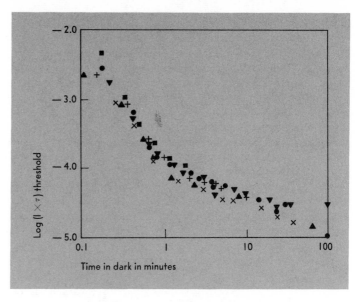

Figure 1-4 Dark-adaptation of a single receptor in the eye of Limulus. *Fall in threshold following a period of light-adaptation. Ordinate: logarithm of the energy (I × τ) of test flash just necessary to elicit the discharge of 1 impulse in a single optic nerve fiber. Intensity (I) of test flash in arbitrary units (1 arb. unit = 25 lumens cm²). Duration (τ) of test flash in seconds. Abscissa: time in the dark (in minutes, plotted on a logarithmic scale) after the cessation of the light-adapting exposure. Light-adapting exposure: 1 arb. unit for 1 second. Five consecutive "runs" were made; in each, the threshold change was followed for an hour or more, after which the light-adapting exposure was repeated and the threshold change was followed again. The various symbols show the results for the separate runs. (Adapted from H. K. Hartline and P. R. McDonald. J. cell. comp. Physiol., 1947, 30, 225–253.)*

we have isolated the relevant variables that act to increase our sensitivity to light in the dark. In many of the topics that we will discuss, we will repeatedly encounter the profitable use of analysis in the physiological study of behavior.

SYNTHESIS: THE TEST OF OUR UNDERSTANDING

Many psychologists (and psychology students) object to a physiological approach to behavior. They say it is of little value to learn about nerve impulses, reflexes, and the anatomy and physiology of the nervous system because all our knowledge of these matters does not help us to predict behavior. Rather, we must study behavioral phenomena, formulate behavioral laws, and let physiology take care of itself. The antiphysiologists say these things because they have been frustrated by having to learn anatomy and physiology only to find later that they really cannot fruitfully apply their knowledge to behavior.

Their criticism is valid. They feel the need for synthesis, but it is often lacking. In psychology, physiological knowledge is seldom used to predict and control behavior; when it is employed, it is often incorrectly used. As we mentioned earlier, we feel we understand something when we analyze it—that is, break it down—into simpler, more familiar elements. However, elements derived from one phenomenon are very often incorrectly used by analogy to "explain" other phenomena for which they are inappropriate. For instance,

The Method
of
Physiological
Psychology

since the work of Pavlov, we know that many simple reflexes can be elicited by new stimuli as a result of pairing them with the unconditioned stimuli that ordinarily elicit those reflexes. Many people therefore concluded that these conditioned reflexes were the appropriate elements whose interaction produces complicated forms of learning and thinking. In principle, all learning could be understood as being made up of complex chains of conditioned reflexes. For years, many complicated theoretical chains of reflexes were constructed to explain behavioral-learning phenomena. But they have been of little use in predicting new phenomena in learning, especially when applied to more abstract thinking and reasoning.

In practice, we must test our understanding to see if it is valid. The test of every analysis is synthesis. If the physiological elements of behavior truly explain it, we should be able to combine the elements in different ways, in different amounts, to produce either new forms of behavior or phenomena we had not realized were determined by those elements. On the basis of physiological principles, we should be able to predict the effect of many conditions on hitherto untested forms of behavior. Then we would know our analysis to be correct. In this book, therefore, we shall devote a good deal of attention to the various methods of synthesis and, wherever possible, shall illustrate their correct use.

METHODS OF SYNTHESIS

As far as I have been able to determine, there are four major techniques of synthesis. They are listed below, in what appears to me to be an increasing order of abstractness.

Direct Synthesis

This method is often used in chemistry. When a chemist wishes to determine the nature of an unknown substance, he breaks it down into its components. If his analysis is correct, he should be able to synthesize the original substance by taking the individual components from completely different sources and putting them together under the appropriate environmental conditions. As we will see below, the composition of rhodopsin, one of the visual photopigments, was proven by such a direct synthesis.

Counterexperiment:
Synthesis after Fractionation

This was the favorite method of Claude Bernard, the great French physiologist. In essence, the principle is: When a change occurs after you remove something, put back a fraction of what you have removed. If you restore the original state, the fraction contains the essential ingredient. For instance, as Bernard discovered, after removal of the pancreas, rabbits waste away and die. Transplant a different pancreas anywhere into the body of such a pancreatectomized rabbit, and it lives normally. Therefore, the transplanted pancreas, even without its normal nervous connections, can maintain life. Make an extract of pancreas and inject it daily into a pancreatectomized rabbit, and it too will live normally. Therefore, something in the extract is vital. Continue this process of analysis and synthesis and eventually, as is now well known, you will discover that the hormone insulin, manufactured by islets of Langerhans in the pancreas, cures the otherwise fatal disease of diabetes mellitus. Later, when we discuss the behavior involved in feeding, we will see other examples of the fruitful use of synthesis by counterexperiment.

Synthesis by Model

We can test our understanding of a phenomenon by constructing a model. We build into the model the elements we think are important and also our conception of the way these elements interact to produce the phenomenon. Such models can be purely theoretical, as in mathematical models of learning behavior, in which, after a theoretical analysis, we postulate the essential elements and processes involved, in such a way that they can be described quantitatively. Then, in situations which are simple enough to handle mathematically, we attempt to predict how the behavior will change as the variables are manipulated. We can also construct physical analogies, as the computer engineer does when he tries to simulate the workings of the nervous system with a digital computer. All such models are attempts to duplicate a behavioral phenomenon through the workings of a model which embodies its essential elements. In our discussion of frequency discrimination in hearing, we will see other examples of synthesis by model.

Synthesis by Prediction

If we have correctly analyzed the elements of a given form of behavior, we should be able to predict which variables will control them, and the way the behavior will change as these variables are manipulated experimentally. This is the most common experimental test of an analysis by synthesis.

THE USE OF MULTIPLE TECHNIQUES TO MEASURE THE SAME THING

Our ideas change. Even though we correctly use the experimental method to search for "facts," what we believe firmly today we may well discard tomorrow. This has been the history of the growth of our knowledge, and it will probably be so in the future. One reason why this is so is aptly given in the old Oriental tale of the six blind men who encounter an elephant for the first time. The first felt the elephant's side, saying, "It feels like a wall." The second touched the elephant's tusk, and said, "It feels like a spear." The third, feeling the trunk, said, "It is like a snake." The fourth felt the knee and said, "It is like a tree." The fifth felt the ear and said, "It is like a fan." The sixth, feeling the tail, said, "It is like a rope."

In science, we are all blind men trying to grasp the unknown. We stumble on some fact, but our view of it greatly depends on the technique we use to find and measure it. As the great physiologist Pierre Flourens put it, "Everything in experimental research depends on the method, for it is the method which gives the results. A new method leads to new results; a rigorous method to precise results; a vague method has never led to anything but confused results." In the parable of the blind men, a scientific finding might be interpreted entirely differently if we revealed another aspect of the same phenomenon by a different method.

This lesson was first pointed out to me by Georg von Békésy, the 1961 Nobel Prize winner in Physiology and Medicine. I once asked him how he solved the problem of the temporary nature of scientific research. He said, "I never publish a finding until I have measured the phenomenon by at least five different methods. Then I know how much of what I think is determined by the particular method used. I expect a fact determined this way to stand unchanged for about 50 years. By that time, radically new methods will probably be available which may then alter the picture."

This is not only the best advice I know about how to do scientific research, it is also the best way of evaluating a scientific "fact." Time and again in the course of this book, we will see repeated illustrations of a change in our interpretations as a result of an improvement in scientific technique. This is why so many scientists spend so much time developing new techniques to measure the same thing. Therefore, wherever possible we shall try to build our beliefs about the physiological basis of behavior on facts that have been determined by multiple techniques. This procedure is fundamental to the correct use of the experimental method in physiological psychology.

Examples of Synthesis

Now let us see how we can apply our methods of analysis and synthesis to the problem of human night vision. We found the phenomenon of dark-adaptation to be present in the activity of an isolated single optic nerve fiber of the horseshoe crab, and we concluded that dark-adaptation occurred in the photochemical and nervous processes that were set up when, in response to light, a receptor generated activity in the optic fiber. Let us analyze still further.

It has been recognized, since the work of Boll in 1876, that the receptors in the eye contain photosensitive pigments. There are two kinds of receptors, rods and cones, and these two provide the anatomical basis for the *duplexity theory* of vision. The rods are believed to function mainly in dim illumination for night vision. They contain rhodopsin, or visual purple, so-called because it absorbs light most easily in the green part of the spectrum, reflecting the remainder, which appears purple. The cones function at high intensity for vision in bright daylight. They contain slightly different pigments.

Human Spectral Sensitivity Duplicated in Spectral Absorption of Isolated Photopigments. To excite any receptor, light must first be absorbed by a visual pigment. One might expect, therefore, that the capacity of rhodopsin to absorb light from different parts of the spectrum would determine the dark-adapted (scotopic) human spectral-sensitivity curve. As seen in Figure 1-5A, our prediction is confirmed. The scotopic human spectral-sensitivity curve closely parallels the absorption curve of rhodopsin. At high illuminations, when a person is light-adapted, the photopic sensitivity curve parallels the absorption

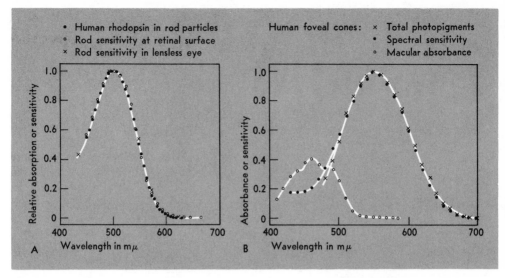

• Human rhodopsin in rod particles   Human foveal cones: × Total photopigments
○ Rod sensitivity at retinal surface   • Spectral sensitivity
× Rod sensitivity in lensless eye   ○ Macular absorbance

Figure 1-5 (A) Absorption spectrum of human rhodopsin, measured in a suspension of rod outer segments, compared with the spectral sensitivity of human rod vision, measured as at the retinal surface. The latter data involve either the average scotopic luminosity corrected for ocular transmission, or uncorrected measurements of the spectral sensitivity of rod vision in the aphakic (lensless) eye. (G. Wald and P. K. Brown. Science, *1958, 127, 222–226.) (B) Difference spectrum of the total photopigments of the human fovea, compared with the spectral sensitivity of foveal vision, measured as at the level of the cones. The luminosity curve, corrected for transmission through the media of the eye, agrees with the difference spectrum of the foveal photopigments (cones) down to about 510 mμ. Below this wavelength the difference spectrum falls off, owing to the formation of colored products of bleaching. (P. K. Brown and G. Wald.* Nature, *1963, 200, 37–43.)*

curve of human cone pigments (see Figure 1-5B), thus supporting our belief that cones function in daylight and rods operate in dim illumination. Rhodopsin is most sensitive to green light (500 mμ), cone pigments to yellow light (550 mμ), and this difference is reflected in the shift in our sensitivity from yellowish to greenish light (Purkinje shift) when we are dark-adapted.

Direct Chemical Synthesis
of Rhodopsin from Separate Components

George Wald and his co-workers at Harvard University have continued this analysis. They have shown that in the presence of light rhodopsin is bleached into orange intermediate substances (lumi- and meta-rhodopsin) which in turn (see Figure 1-6) form retinene (a yellow pigment) and opsin (a complex protein residue). The retinene is reduced to Vitamin A by the enzyme alcohol dehydrogenase, working together with the coenzyme DPN (cozymase).

In darkness, the reaction goes the other way: Retinene and opsin combine to form rhodopsin; Vitamin A is then oxidized to form more retinene, and so

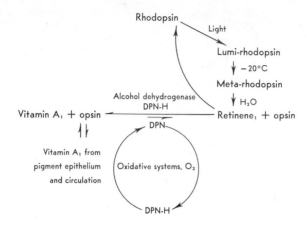

Figure 1-6 Schematic representation of the rhodopsin system in the eye. (R. Hubbard and G. Wald. Proc. nat. Acad. Sci., *1951, 37, 69–79.)*

on until all the opsin has been used up to restore the high, dark-adapted concentration of rhodopsin. The direct synthesis to prove this analysis was made by Hubbard and Wald in 1951. They took the individual elements from completely different sources, put them all together, and produced natural rhodopsin. A system containing purified opsin from the retinas of cattle, crystalline alcohol dehydrogenase derived from horse liver, Vitamin A from fish liver oil, and cozymase from yeast, when brought together in solution, formed rhodopsin. This is a beautiful example of the test of an analysis by direct synthesis. It supports our belief that a particular photochemical process is involved in dark-adaptation. In the dark-adapted human eye, the concentration of rhodopsin rises, increasing our sensitivity to light. But without Vitamin A, rhodopsin cannot be formed and night vision is impaired.

In summary, we have seen that any physiological attempt to understand behavior first breaks it down (analysis) then puts it back together (synthesis). We will use this approach in every topic we discuss. We will always start with the behavior that interests us, break it down into appropriate elements, then show how those elements determine the way many variables affect that behavior. In the process, since the elements are units of nervous-system function as well as units of behavior, we will learn how the nervous system controls behavior.

Principles
of Nervous-System
Function

As we have seen, human visual judgment and response can parallel closely the way a simple fragment of the visual system works. Fundamental principles of nervous function can, therefore, be revealed in psychophysical phenomena. Many of these principles are common to all levels of nervous function. Let us consider some.

15

2

The Bunsen-Roscoe Law: Temporal Summation. From psychophysical experiments with human observers, it has been found that at any given intensity, the longer a brief flash of light is kept on, the easier it is to see. The threshold intensity (I) is inversely proportional to flash duration (T) for flashes lasting up to 100 milliseconds $(= .1 \text{ sec})$. This relationship, $I = C/T$ can also be written as $IT = C$, $(C$ is a constant) in which form it is known as the Bunsen-Roscoe law. Such experimental data are shown in Figure 2-1. When plotted on log-log coordinates, as they are in Figure 2-1, any inverse relationship such as $IT = C$ will appear as a straight line of negative slope. (If we take the log of $IT = C$, we get $\log I + \log T = \log C$. Since $\log C$ is a new constant (call it K), $\log I = K - \log T$, a straight line with a slope of -1.) The effect of a light flash, then, summates over time (temporal summation).

Ricco's Law: Spatial Summation. At any given duration, the greater the area (A) of a spot of light, the easier it is to see. This psychophysically obtained relationship, $IA = C$, is known as Ricco's law. As shown in Figure 2-2, it holds for retinal areas up to about 1 degree. Thus the effect of light on the retina summates over area (spatial summation).

Mach Bands: Mutual Inhibition. As our eyes become dark-adapted, our sensitivity to the brightness of light increases, but our visual acuity decreases. As shown in Figure 2-3, in bright light we can detect an extremely narrow black wire on a bright background. As we become dark-adapted, in dim illumination the wire must be much wider to be detected. In dark-adaptation our visual system shifts from the use of cones to rods. It is known that visual receptors, widely spaced over the retina, converge in their connections to other cells in the retina which relay their signals toward

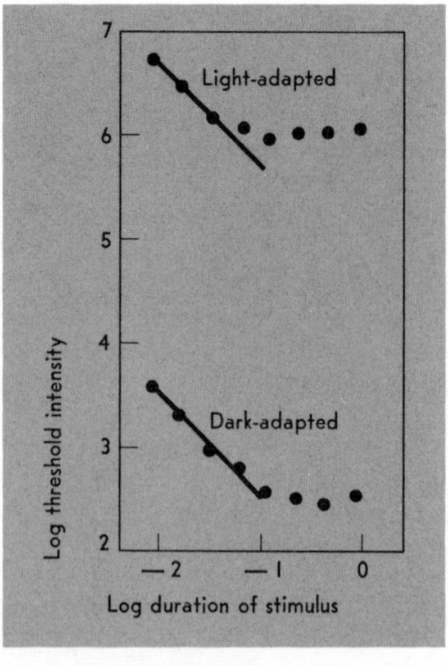

Figure 2-1 Temporal summation. The top curve represents human visual thresholds in the light-adapted state (log background intensity = 7.83), and the lower curve in the completely dark-adapted state. Note that threshold decreases as flash duration increases. A circular spot of light (27.6 deg² in area) centered 6°30′ from the fixation point was used. Durations in seconds. The straight lines have a slope of −1. (Adapted from H. B. Barlow. J. Physiol., 1958, 141, 337–350.)

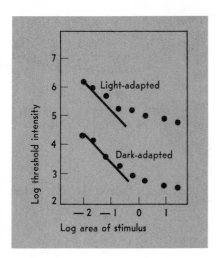

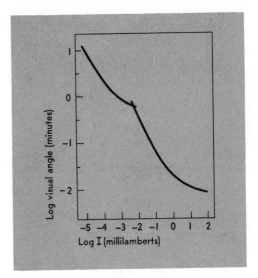

Figure 2-2 Spatial summation. The top curve represents human visual thresholds in the light-adapted state (log background intensity = 5.94), and the lower curve in the completely dark-adapted state. Note that threshold decreases as the area of the spot of light increases. A light flash lasting 0.93 sec was used, centered 6°30′ from the fixation point. Areas in degrees. The straight lines have a slope of −1. (Adapted from H. B. Barlow. J. Physiol., 1958, 141, 337–350.)

Figure 2-3 Threshold visual angle subtended by the thickness of wire which is just resolved against its background. The thickness necessary to be perceived decreases as background intensity increases; upper section of curve is for rod vision; lower for cone vision. (Reprinted by permission of Rockefeller Univ. Press from S. Hecht and E. Mintz. J. gen. Physiol., 1939, 22, 593–612.)

the brain. It is thought, therefore, that rods are more useful for light-gathering than for discrimination of fine detail and might summate the effects of light-stimulation over wider areas of the retina than do cones. If true, this could explain our decreased visual acuity when our eyes are dark-adapted.

The human eye exaggerates differences. Due to the diffusion of light as it passes through the aqueous and vitreous humors in the eye before it strikes the retina, any spot of light, no matter how sharply defined, always scatters a fringe that shades gradually into blackness. However, we actually perceive a bright spot with a sharply defined edge, and are unaware of a fuzzy fringe. Somehow the eye sharpens up the transitional fringe area between light and dark so that we see it as an abrupt change, a sharp edge. This phenomenon is an example of *simultaneous contrast*.

If we build a model to enlarge the transition area between light and dark, we can magnify the sharpening process. A white star-shape on a black background can be constructed on a cardboard disk as in Figure 2-4A. The center area is uniformly white, and the outermost area at the edge of the disk is uniformly black. In the transition area, the amount of white in the rays of the star decreases uniformly to blackness at the surround. When the disk is

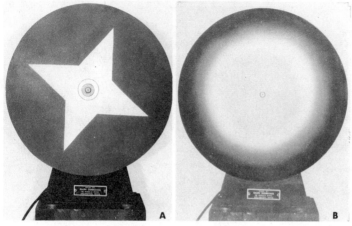

Figure 2-4 Model for producing visual Mach bands. A cardboard disk is constructed in which a white star shape is drawn on a black background. (A) On the left, the stationary disk is seen mounted on a wheel ready to be rotated. (B) On the right is a photograph of the rapidly rotating disk.

rotated rapidly, the amount of light reflected by the central white field is uniformly bright in the center, then decreases smoothly through increasing gray to the uniform black of the surround. If we perceive only what is supplied by the physical stimulus, we should see a white center, a transition zone growing steadily darker, then shading smoothly into a black surround.

Figure 2-4 shows such a disk. On the left, it is stationary; on the right, it is rotating. The physical light pattern in the photograph is shown by the solid line in Figure 2-5, but the gray line shows how it actually appears to us. At the edge of the center field, where the light begins to decrease, we see a band of white that is actually brighter than any other part of the central white area. At the inner edge of the dark surround, where no further decrease in light occurs, we see a very black band, blacker than the outer portion of the dark surround. This phenomenon was described by Ernst Mach in the nineteenth century, and the areas of enhanced brightness and darkness are known as Mach bands.

Figure 2-5 Schematic illustration of visual Mach bands. The solid black line represents the actual physical stimulus presented to the eye by the rotating disk in Figure 2-4B. The center is uniformly bright, the surround is uniformly dark, and the transition zone (the rays of the star) shades uniformly from bright to dark. The gray line represents the perceived sensation produced by such a physical stimulus. At the transition areas of the stimulus, Mach bands are seen: a bright band around the center area where the stimulus begins to grow dark, and a black band at the edge of the surround. See text for explanation.

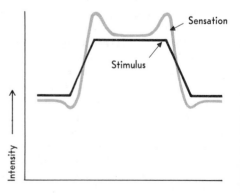

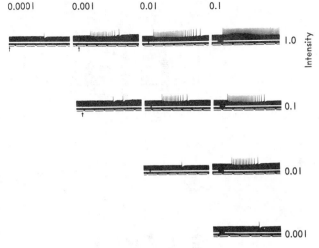

0.0001   0.001   0.01   0.1

1.0

0.1

0.01

0.001

Intensity

Figure 2-6 The Bunsen-Roscoe law of temporal summation (IT = C) demonstrated in the eye of Limulus. As measured by the number of impulses generated in a single optic nerve fiber, a light flash of a given intensity is more effective with increasing duration. At any intensity, for durations up to 0.1 sec, when the product of I × T is constant, a constant number of impulses is generated in the optic fiber. (H. K. Hartline. J. cell. comp. Physiol., 1934, 5, 229–247.)

*Physiological Analysis
of Psychophysical Phenomena*

Temporal Summation in the Crab Eye.   Let us see whether physiological analysis can help us to understand these psychophysical phenomena. We will again use Hartline's single-receptor/single-optic-nerve-fiber preparation from the horseshoe crab. As shown in Figure 2-6, to judge by the number of nerve impulses elicited by a flash of light, the longer the flash, the more effectively is the eye stimulated. In the crab eye, as in the human eye, $IT = C$ holds perfectly up to 100 milliseconds. Therefore, temporal summation can occur in the simple receptor/optic-fiber preparation. It is known from photochemistry that $IT = C$ is a fundamental physical law governing the absorption of light by any pigment. The longer the flash, the more light is absorbed. Therefore, temporal summation of light occurs in each retinal receptor. It is faithfully reproduced all the way along the nervous system and is reflected in visual discrimination as the Bunsen-Roscoe law. As described later, temporal summation is characteristic of all nerve cells—up to a point, a brief stimulus is more effective in exciting a nerve cell the longer it lasts.

Spatial Summation in the Cat Retina.   In the crab eye, a large spot of light is not more effective than a small one in generating activity in the optic nerve fiber. Ricco's law cannot be demonstrated there. To study Ricco's law, we must therefore turn to a more complex eye, such as that of the cat. The cat, like all vertebrates, has an inverted retina. The receptors point away from the source of light, instead of toward it, as in the crab eye. As seen in Figure 2-7, the vertebrate retina is composed of layers of nervous cells. The outermost (furthest from and facing away from the lens) is the receptor layer, made up of densely packed rods and cones. These connect to a layer of bipolar cells, which in turn make contact (synapse) with the cells of the next layer, the ganglion cells. Thus, light has to travel through several layers of cells (fortunately, nearly transparent) to get to the re-

Nervous-
System
Function

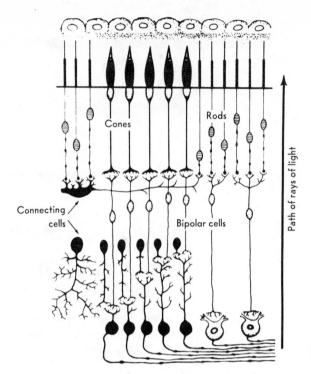

Figure 2-7 Simplified schematic illustration of the nerve-cell network in a vertebrate retina. (Adapted from S. R. Detwiler. Sigma Xi Quarterly, *1941, 29,112–129.)*

ceptors. The nerve fibers from the ganglion cells collect at one place in the retina (the optic disk) and travel into the brain in a bundle which makes up the optic nerve. Since there are many more receptors than there are ganglion cells (in the human eye, for instance, there are about 120 million rods and cones, but only 1 million or so ganglion cells), there is typically an anatomical *convergence* of many receptors on each bipolar, and of several bipolars on each ganglion cell. Thus, we have the anatomical basis for spatial summation: By convergence, weak light stimulation affecting receptors over a wide area of the retina can be intensified by simultaneously bombarding a single ganglion cell. The horizontal interconnections between receptors, bipolars, and ganglion cells can be quite complex, affording much opportunity for spatial interaction on the retina. There is convergence throughout the retina except in some parts of the fovea (that area of the retina, consisting entirely of cones, where a visual image is most sharply focused), where direct one-to-one connections have been found from cone to bipolar to ganglion cell.

How can we measure the way light stimulation interacts on different areas of the retina? Ideally, to reveal the process of spatial summation in its purest form we should reduce the system to its simplest elements: Find two receptors that converge on a single bipolar cell, stimulate and measure the effect of light on each receptor separately, measure their individual effect on the bipolar, and then see if stimulating them simultaneously will increase the net effect on the bipolar cell. If Ricco's law held in this simple system, and all convergent interactions in the eye were similar, we could assume that the variables involved in the convergence of receptors on bipolar cells are responsible for spatial summation. If not, we would have to include more of the visual system—for instance, the ganglion cells in the next layer, and so on—until we had the simplest system in which Ricco's law appeared.

Unfortunately, the physiological techniques now available do not permit us to study such an ideally simple system. Our aim is to measure the activity of a given receptor cell and to detect its effect on a bipolar cell without confusing them with any of their neighbors. But because receptors and bipolars lie densely packed together in the retina, if we place an ordinary wire electrode among these cells, the electrode will simultaneously detect the changes in potential produced by many of them. If they are all active randomly (out of phase), positive potentials will cancel out negative ones, and little or no activity will be recorded. If a majority is active simultaneously, a compound potential will be detected, but we will be unable to isolate the activity of any particular cell. In the crab optic nerve, that problem was solved by cutting all the fibers until only one remained intact. The electrode placed on the nerve bundle thus recorded only the activity of the remaining intact fiber.

An alternative approach is to diminish the size of the recording tip of the electrode, so that it will pick up only activity in a cell lying right next to it. Such a *microelectrode* was developed in 1949, when the improved electronic amplification systems required by such tiny electrodes became available. Typically, a glass capillary tube, whose tip is drawn out to a point as small as 1 micron across, is used. The tube is filled with a conducting salt solution. More recently, insulated metal microelectrodes, with exposed tips electrolytically polished down to 0.1 micron in diameter, have been developed and used. The size of the nerve cell is also important, for if it is too small or its nerve impulses are too weak, the recording system will be unable to detect its activity reliably. With the systems now available, we can easily record activity in cells of 50-100 microns in diameter, but smaller ones are more difficult to study. It is, therefore, unfortunate (from the point of view of scientific study) that the retinal rods and cones are about 1 micron in diameter, and are buried in the deepest layer of the retina, where the fragile tip of the microelectrode cannot easily penetrate. The bipolar cells are also difficult to reach. Only the ganglion cells, the third link in the chain from receptor to brain, lie exposed on the surface of the retina, and only the activity of the larger ones (50 microns or larger) can be readily sampled. Still, their function is vastly simpler than that of the entire nervous system involved in a visual judgment, so we can learn a great deal by studying the way receptors in a given area of the retina converge in their effect on a single ganglion cell.

Such a study, using cats, was done by Stephen Kuffler and his co-workers at The Johns Hopkins University in 1954. First, to prevent the cat's eye from moving, the eye muscles were cut and the anesthetized cat's head and eyelid were fixed in a rigid frame. A hypodermic needle tube was pushed through the wall of the eye behind the lens, and the microelectrode was inserted through it into the eye until the tip just rested against the retina, right next to a ganglion cell (the arrangement is shown in Figure 2-8).

Figure 2-8 Arrangement for retinal studies from the unopened eye of the deeply anesthetized cat. The Multibeam-Ophthalmoscope contains three light sources (A,B,C) channelled into the eye. The retina is observed through the ocular (D). The whole upper portion of the equipment can be freely rotated and tilted for exploration of a large portion of the retina. The eye is fixed to a circular ring which is part of the microelectrode holder. (S. W. Kuffler. Cold Spring Harbor Symp. Quant. Biol., 1952, 17, 281–292.)

To illuminate areas of the cat retina as small as 0.1 mm in diameter, Kuffler's group designed a multibeam ophthalmoscope, an instrument which uses a mirror to reflect a tiny beam of light into the eye. Through a hole in the mirror, the observer can look along the beam of light and see the surface it illuminates. Using a magnifying lens, he can see an enlarged image of the illuminated area of the retina, as shown in Figure 2-9. He can then shine spots of light of various size and intensity on retinal receptors situated at different distances from a ganglion cell, and simultaneously record their effect on its activity.

The receptors closest to the ganglion cell are most effective in stimulating it. For a radius of half a millimeter around, however, stimulation of distant receptors increases the activity of the ganglion cell. As shown in Figure 2-10, increasing the area of a spot of light up to 1 mm in diameter causes the ganglion cell to fire more readily, as though in response to a brighter light. On a log-log plot, the decrease in threshold as the diameter of the spot grows is a straight line with a slope of −1. Thus, Ricco's law of spatial summation, $IA = C$, is produced in the retina by anatomical convergence of receptors on each ganglion cell, and in cats the law holds for retinal areas equivalent to those in human beings.

Mutual Inhibition in the Cat Retina.

If the diameter of the light spot is increased still further, a strange thing happens. As shown in Figure 2-10 (top curve), the larger spot, instead of becoming easier to see, becomes less visible. The spot must be made more intense in order to stimulate the ganglion cell. Indeed, when it is 3 mm in diameter, a spot must be almost 10 times more intense than a 1 mm spot to be equally effective in firing the ganglion cell. Clearly, then, adding light in the surround (the area 1 to 3 mm away from the center) subtracts from the effectiveness of light in the center. If tiny (0.1 mm diameter) spots of light are used for stimulation, we find that the *retinal receptive field* of a given ganglion cell (that area on the retina which affects its activity)

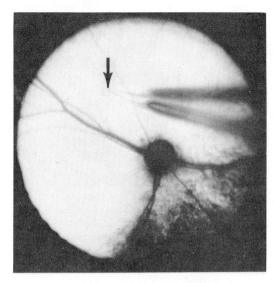

Figure 2-9 View of the cat's retina in the region of the optic disc, with the microelectrode in position. The upper dark line on the right is the shadow of the microelectrode shaft. Arrow marks the point of contact. (S. W. Kuffler. Cold Spring Harbor Symp. Quant. Biol., 1952, 17, 281–292.)

Figure 2-10 Spatial summation in ganglion cell of cat eye. The curves represent the change of threshold intensity of light for an off-center unit as the diameter of the white stimulating spot is changed. The top curve was made in the light-adapted state (0.08 foot-candles, blue-green light), and the bottom one in the completely dark-adapted state. The dashed line has the slope predicted by Ricco's law of area summation. (Adapted from H. B. Barlow, R. Fitzhugh, and S. W. Kuffler. J. Physiol., 1957, 137, 338–354.)

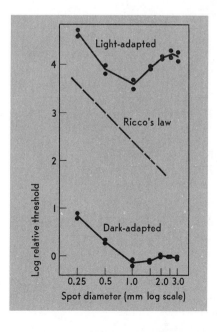

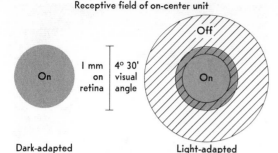

Receptive field of on-center unit

On

1 mm
on
retina

4° 30'
visual
angle

Off

On

Dark-adapted

Light-adapted

Figure 2-11 Suggested organ-
ization of the receptive field
of an on-center ganglion cell in
the dark- and light-adapted
states. "On" or "Off" responses
to a flash are obtained when the
light stimulus falls in the cor-
respondingly labelled regions of
the field. (H. B. Barlow, R.
Fitzhugh, and S. W. Kuffler. J.
Physiol., 1957, 137, 338–354.)

is composed of two parts: a center and a surround, both mutually antagonistic in their effects on the ganglion cell. For example, as shown in Figure 2-11, a spot of light turned on in the center causes the ganglion cell to fire rapidly. When the light is turned off, the rate of firing ceases. A spot of light in the surround of that cell (Figure 2-11) does the opposite. It *inhibits* the activity of the ganglion cell: As long as light is on in the surround, the spontaneous rate of firing in the ganglion cell is much less, or is even decreased to zero. Then, at the termination of light in the surround, the ganglion cell responds with a burst of rapid firing: It is *released from inhibition*. Thus, a ganglion cell with an "on" center has an "off" surround.

Other ganglion cells are opposite in type: They are "off" cells, inhibited by light in the center, firing only when it is turned off. Light in their surround is also antagonistic to the center; it produces an "on" response. Of what value is such a system of mutual inhibition?

Change in Spatial Interaction with Dark-Adaptation. There is one condition in which the surround does not appear to operate, which perhaps can give us a clue to its function. Figure 2-10 demonstrates that when the eye of a cat has been dark-adapted, the threshold for a spot of light is lowered. In addition, as in the light-adapted eye, spatial summation lowers the threshold as spot diameter increases up to 1 mm. But further increase in the spot size produces no further change in the dark-adapted threshold. It does not rise, as in the light-adapted eye, nor does it decrease further. This result tells us two things: First, in the cat eye, summation does not appear to occur over a greater area in the dark-adapted eye (the summation area is 1 mm in both the light- and the dark-adapted eye); second, the antagonistic surround does not function (there is no rise in threshold) when the eye is dark-adapted. If the human eye is similar to the cat's eye (after all, Ricco's law does hold in both), then spatial summation may not be the only factor involved in the poor visual acuity of night vision (see Figure 2-3).

Mutual Inhibition and Visual Acuity

What is also lacking in night vision is the contribution of the antagonistic surround. Perhaps acuity is poorer at night, not merely because of increased areal summation, but also for lack of an antagonistic sharpening mechanism that serves to clarify details by exaggerating differences in the intensity of stimulation on adjacent receptors. Thus, the fuzzy fringe around a spot of light produced by scattering in the eye could be eliminated if weaker stimulation of adjacent receptors was suppressed by stronger stimulation of the neighboring cells. Actually, such a mutual lateral antagonism should produce Mach bands wherever there exists a sufficient difference in the intensity of stimulation. In a uniformly stimulated sheet of receptors, all exert an equally strong mutual inhibition on each other, and a damped uniform level of excitation results. However, the cells at the edge of a bright field receive less inhibition from their weakly excited neighbors in the shadow. They therefore fire more rapidly than their strongly inhibited neighbors toward the center of the field, and appear more strongly stimulated. Thus, one sees an exaggeratedly bright band at the edge of light. The same process occurs at the transition from gray to black. The cells at the edge of the black field are more strongly inhibited by their gray (more strongly illuminated) neighbors and so a dark black ring is seen.

If these speculations are correct, then Mach bands should be demonstrable in a visual system in which inhibition is the only type of lateral spatial interaction.

Synthesis of Mach Band in the Crab Eye.   It is now known that the eye of *Limulus*, the horseshoe crab, possesses such a system. As we mentioned earlier, no spatial summation occurs in the *Limulus* eye. Shining light on one retinal element does not facilitate the effectiveness of light in any of the neighboring elements. Nor, until recently, had any anatomical interconnections been found, thus supporting the idea that each receptor/optic-fiber unit is independent of all the others. However, more recent anatomical techniques, using the increased magnification provided by the electron microscope, have been able to demonstrate a lateral plexus—a fine

Figure 2-12   Section through part of a lateral eye of an adult Limulus, *perpendicular to the cornea, showing the heavily pigmented portions of the ommatidia (upper border of the section), the bundles of nerve fibers emerging from them, the plexus of interconnecting fibers, and a portion of the optic nerve (bottom of figure). The chitinous cornea with the attached crystalline cones of the ommatidia had been stripped away prior to fixation. (Reprinted by permission of the Rockefeller Univ. Press from H. K. Hartline, H. G. Wagner, and F. Ratliff.* J. gen. Physiol., *1956, 39, 651–673.)*

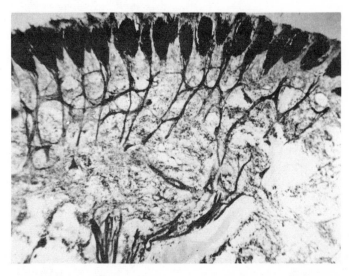

meshwork of tiny fibers—interconnecting the optic nerve fibers, as pictured in Figure 2-12.

Floyd Ratliff and H. Keffer Hartline, in recent work at the Rockefeller Institute, have been able to show that light shining on any retinal element in the crab eye inhibits the effect of light on its neighbors. The closer the receptors are, the more strongly they inhibit each other.

It is not possible to record simultaneously from all of the fibers in the *Limulus* optic nerve, so we cannot test for Mach bands directly by presenting a stationary contrast pattern to the eye. However, in a single-fiber preparation, we can duplicate the effect of looking at a step pattern of light, a bright area next to a darker one, by moving the pattern past the fiber's receptor. If the eye is masked so light strikes only the ommatidium attached to the optic fiber being recorded from, its rate of firing forms a simple step-shaped curve (Figure 2-13). The rate of firing is high in the bright area and falls abruptly to a lower level as the dim area is moved over it. If the eye is unmasked, however, allowing neighboring receptors to

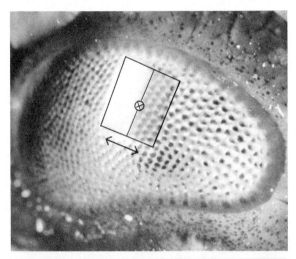

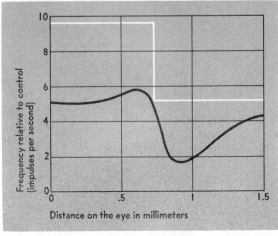

Figure 2-13   Contrast heightening at contours is demonstrated by letting "step" pattern of light, a bright area next to a darker one, fall on the Limulus *eye (top). (F. Ratliff,* Mach Bands. *San Francisco: Holden-Day, Inc., 1965, p. 162.) If the eye is masked so light strikes only one ommatidium, a recording of its output forms a simple step-shaped curve (top curve in bottom half of figure) as the pattern is moved across the eye. If the eye is unmasked, the output of the single ommatidium is inhibited in varying degrees by the light striking its neighbors. The net effect (lower curve) is to heighten contrast at light-dark boundaries. (W. H. Miller, F. Ratliff, and H. K. Hartline.* How cells receive stimuli. Copyright © 1961 by *Scientific American, Inc. All rights reserved.)*

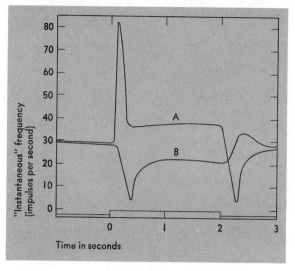

Figure 2-14 Stimulation of one Limulus *receptor (A) produces inhibitory effects on its neighbor (B). Receptor B was illuminated steadily throughout the period shown. Receptor A received illumination steadily until time 0, when it was increased for 2 seconds, and then decreased to the original level. Excitation in A produces inhibition in B. (Reprinted from Ratliff in W. A. Rosenblith (ed.).*

Sensory Communication *by permission of The MIT Press, Cambridge, Mass.. Copyright © 1961 by the Massachusetts Institute of Technology. All rights reserved.)*

inhibit each other, heightened contrast is seen. As the dim area approaches the receptor we are recording from, it shows an increased burst of firing (like a bright Mach band) because it is not as strongly inhibited by its now dimly lit neighbors. Conversely, if a bright edge is moved along after a dim field, our fiber shows a dark band (a decrease in its firing rate) when its now brightly lit neighbors begin to inhibit it more strongly. Thus, heightened spatial contrast is a property of a purely inhibitory system. It is produced by mutual lateral inhibition.

Hartline and Ratliff have very clearly demonstrated such mutual inhibition by recording the effect of light stimulation in one receptor (A) on the firing rate of its neighbor (B). As shown in Figure 2-14, shining a brighter light on A causes it to fire rapidly and then to decrease to a stable level (adaptation). Turning the light off causes its rate to drop sharply, then return to its baseline. The pattern of firing in the optic nerve of its steadily illuminated neighbor B is the mirror image of A. Any increase in A's rate causes a decrease in B's. B's excessive discharge after A's light is turned off illustrates the *rebound* phenomenon—excessive activity after a release from inhibition.

SIMILAR PRINCIPLES IN OTHER SENSORY SYSTEMS

*Frequency Discrimination
in Hearing and Skin Sensations:
Synthesis by Model*

By analysis, we have seen that the increased sensitivity that is exemplified in visual perception by the Bunsen-Roscoe law and Ricco's law is due to temporal and spatial summation in the retina. Sensory discrimination, as exemplified by visual acuity, is

Nervous-
System
Function

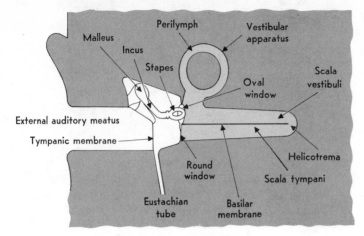

Figure 2-15   Schematic human ear. Sound waves enter the external meatus, and move the tympanic membrane (eardrum) which sets the 3 ossicles in motion. When the stapes footplate moves in, the fluid (perilymph) in the cochlea flows toward the helicotrema, making the round window membrane bulge out. (From G. v. Békésy and W. A. Rosenblith in S. S. Stevens (ed.) Handbook of Experimental Psychology. *New York: Wiley, 1951, p. 1076.)*

sharpened by the process of *mutual inhibition*. These are fundamental properties of even the simplest neural networks and should therefore be common to all sensory systems, and all parts of the nervous system at any level.

For example, we are able to hear sounds ranging in frequency from 20 cycles per second to 20,000 cycles per second. Over part of this tremendous frequency range, we are able to discriminate between two tones differing by as little as 5 cycles per second. In 1863, Helmholtz suggested how the ear might perform an analysis of sound frequency. The mechanical vibrations of sound waves are transmitted from the ear drum along the chain of bones (the ossicles, called the malleus, incus, and stapes) to the cochlea in the middle ear (Figure 2-15). The receptors for hearing are the sensitive hair cells which lie along the basilar membrane in the cochlea. If we assume that the basilar membrane is made up of a tautly stretched sheet of fibers, then, like tuned piano strings, different segments of the basilar membrane could resonate to different frequencies of sound, thereby stimulating separate hair cells at each frequency. High tones should cause the stiff narrow segment of the basilar membrane near the oval window to vibrate, whereas low tones should cause a resonant vibration in the wider, more flexible part of the basilar membrane further away. Much evidence supports such a place theory of frequency discrimination. As shown in Figure 2-16, precise measurements of the vibration pattern of the basilar membrane by Georg von Békésy have proven that the ear mechanically generates a traveling wave in the cochlea whose place of peak amplitude along the basilar membrane varies with the frequency of the sound. As Helmholtz predicted, the stiff part of the basilar membrane vibrates most strongly for high tones, and the soft part most strongly for low tones. But Békésy's measurements of the tension, elasticity, and degree of coupling of the fibers of the basilar membrane also made it clear that there is no possibility of a fine resonant ("piano wire") tuning as conceived by Helmholtz. And the traveling wave is so broad in shape that

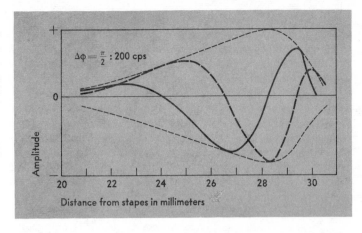

Figure 2-16 Detail of the form of the traveling wave produced on the basilar membrane by a 200-cps tone. The solid line shows the wave at one instant in time within a cycle. The heavy dashed line represents its form and position 1.25 msec later. (G. v. Békésy. J. acoust. Soc. Amer., 1947, 19, 452–460.)

the amounts of excitation generated all along the broad peak could not possibly produce the fine tuning required to account for our precise discrimination of sound. Békésy knew then that there must be some kind of inhibitory sharpening performed by the nervous system in response to the broad, mechanical traveling-wave stimulus.

But how to measure it? It is just not practical to record simultaneously from all the auditory nerve fibers that would be needed to demonstrate lateral interactions. It might be possible to search higher in the auditory system for third-order neurons comparable to the ganglion cells Kuffler stimulated in the retina, but one would have to stimulate small portions of the very inaccessible basilar membrane differentially and precisely if one hoped to show the nature of the stimulus transformation performed by the nervous system. Békésy felt that there must be some other way. Let's try to follow his line of reasoning.

Clearly, our nervous system performs a sharpening: Given only the broad area of mechanical stimulation produced on the basilar membrane by traveling waves, we do hear very slight differences in frequency. The stapes rocks back and forth in the oval window of the cochlea reproducing the vibration pattern of the sound and generating traveling waves in the fluid-filled vestibular canal of the cochlea. These waves cause that highly differentiated piece of skin, the basilar membrane, to bend and flap and stimulate the hair cells on it. Wait a minute! Can we really listen with our skin? After all, the basilar membrane is derived embryonically from skin and is merely a differentiation of its basic structure. But that differentiation is just what enables us to hear—the ear amplifies the tiny mechanical sound vibrations into bending and shearing forces on the basilar membrane and spreads them out in space. Our external skin is not sensitive enough to detect such tiny sound vibrations. Well, then, why not build a giant ear for our skin to listen with? Amplify the mechanical vibrations produced by the basilar membrane and spread them out over a large surface of skin. Then let the brain perform the transformation of the input on the skin just the way it does in the ear. We can ask an observer what he feels just the way we ask him what he hears. In fact, we can do this for every phenomenon of hearing in order to see the differences and similarities between auditory and skin sensations. What is common to them both are properties probably general to all parts of the nervous system. What is unique to hearing will reveal the nature of the specializations in the hearing mechanism developed in evolution.

What kind of a model shall we use to synthesize the performance of the ear? Most models are oversimplified analogies—although often useful, they merely embody our theoretical conception of how something works. They contain only those properties we are clever enough to endow them with in advance and can therefore usually produce only a few approximations of real-life phenomena. Is there a way of building a model of the inner ear, the bony tube of the cochlea with its flexible basilar membrane, that will really work like the ear and produce real phenomena we have not yet even dreamed of?

When an engineer designs a new ship or an airplane, he must often test out his ideas before he builds the real thing. Otherwise, if he has made a mistake in design, a million dollars' worth of brand-new ship with its unlucky

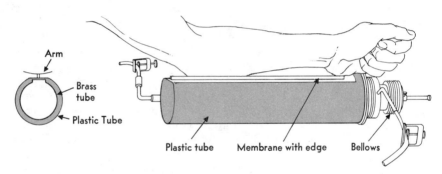

Figure 2-17 Mechanical model of the cochlea, to be applied to the skin of the arm. (Adapted from G. v. Békésy. Science, 1956, 123, 779–783.)

crew may sink to the bottom of the sea. To solve this problem, he uses *dimensional analysis* to build a model. He uses the measurements from his plans and scales them down so that he builds an exact miniature version of his dream ship. The way this model behaves in wind tunnels, in artificial storm conditions, and so on, will accurately reproduce what his full-size ship will do. Békésy adapted the technique of dimensional analysis to build his model of the cochlea. He measured every aspect of the cochlea that was relevant to the production of traveling waves on the basilar membrane—the length and diameter of the cochlea, the stiffness, coupling, and elasticity of every point along the basilar membrane, and so forth. He then built a simplified, large-scale model of the cochlea, one that incorporated the essential dimensions in correct relation to one another. The cochlea model is shown in Figure 2-17. A driving piston (the stapes) vibrates at frequencies of 40 to 320 cycles per second, a frequency range of three octaves. A bellows (the

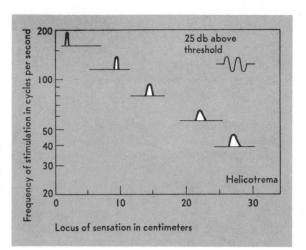

Figure 2-18 The perceived extent of the sensation produced by the cochlea model on the skin of the arm as a function of frequency, for a pulse of 2 waves. (G. v. Békésy. J. acoust. Soc. Amer., 1955, 27, 830–841.)

oval window) transmits these vibrations to a water-filled brass tube (the tympanic canal of the bony cochlea) with a lengthwise slit in it and covered by a plastic sheet (the basilar membrane) which is narrow and stiff near the stapes and wider and more flexible at the other end.

When the stapes is driven by a steady vibration (like a pure tone), the basilar membrane vibrates. Using a stroboscopic light, Békésy was able to "stop" the motion of the waves by flashing at precisely the same frequency and in exactly the same phase as the waves on the basilar membrane. He found that the model does indeed produce traveling waves of broad peaks which vary in location along the model's basilar membrane with the driving frequency of the piston. The amplitude of vibration is much greater than in the ear, and the frequency range is smaller, but the broad traveling waves closely resemble those in the ear. The mechanical ear was ready.

We can see in Figure 2-18 that when the arm of the observer is placed on the basilar membrane of the model, he localizes the sensation in a narrow region of skin even though a broad traveling wave is stimulating the entire length of his forearm. Increasing the frequency of the vibrations causes the sensation to move toward the stapes, just as it does in the ear. Discrimination can be made between tones differing as little as 20 cycles per second, even though the traveling waves they generate differ only slightly in the place of their peak amplitude. A man can indeed listen with his skin.

The basic principle of frequency discrimination by sharpening is shown more clearly by another model (Figure 2-19); which uses a different form of vibration. A box is constructed with 5 holes spaced 2 cm apart. In each hole, a tiny piston can vibrate at a given frequency and amplitude independently of the other pistons. As shown, they are set to vibrate at 20, 40, 80, 160, and 320 cycles per second. The skin of the subject's forearm is pressed firmly against the upper surface of the box and the amplitude of each piston is adjusted so that they feel equally intense—that is, equally loud—in their vibration. Each of them can be identified by its place and its frequency when it alone is vibrating. What does the arm feel when all

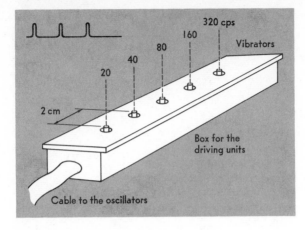

Figure 2-19   Arrangement of a series of vibrators to show inhibition on the skin of the arm. (G. v. Békésy. J. acoust. Soc. Amer., 1957, 29, 1059–1069.)

of them vibrate simultaneously? As shown in Figure 2-20, when their amplitude is equal, the arm feels only the one in the middle—80 cycles per second. The others are not felt at all. They do contribute to the intensity felt in the middle, because when they are turned off, the 80-cycle vibration provided by the middle vibrator feels much less intense. But when all the others vibrate with it, their frequencies and location on the skin are completely inhibited. The touch receptors on the skin are connected to the nervous system by nerve fibers running into the spinal cord. Many side branches interconnect these fibers by a lateral plexus, similar to the horizontal interconnections of the retina. Therefore, principles of spatial summation and inhibition can operate in the skin as they do in the eye. There is clearly a summation because the sensation felt in the middle when all vibrators are on is increased. The difference in peak amplitude of stimulation, created by spatial summation, enables the central area to inhibit the areas on either side. We can demonstrate this easily: If we increase the intensity of any of the vibrators—for instance, 40 cycles per second—so that it is stronger than the rest, the sensation jumps immediately to that point and the only frequency now felt is 40 cycles, not 80. The ear does the same thing—the effect of the peak amplitude of the traveling wave on the basilar membrane is to

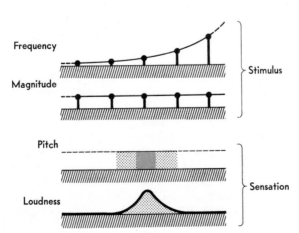

Figure 2-20 The sensory effects of presenting five vibrations to the skin simultaneously, wtih frequency varying as shown. (G. v. Békésy. J. acoust. Soc. Amer., 1957, 29, 1059–1069.)

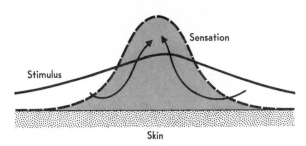

Figure 2-21 An illustration of "funneling" on the skin. The stimulus gradient is sharpened by central summation and lateral inhibition. A similar form occurs in vision. (G. v. Békésy. J. acoust. Soc. Amer., 1958, 30, 399–412.)

inhibit the sensation of stimulation around it, thus sharpening localization on the basilar membrane, and thereby sharpening the frequency discrimination of sound. As shown in Figure 2-21, a slight gradient is sharpened by lateral inhibition and central summation. Békésy calls this process "funneling." It is analogous to the generation of Mach bands by mutual inhibition.

From this beautiful example of synthesis by model, we see that many of the same principles of nervous function operate in skin, ear, and eye. Békésy has also recently demonstrated analogous phenomena in the senses of taste and smell. Spatial summation and mutual inhibition are general characteristics of nervous-system function.

The Neuron
and the Synapse

We have seen that some psychophysical judgments clearly reflect the operation of several processes in the nervous system: excitation, inhibition, facilitation by temporal and spatial summation, and sharpening of contrast by mutual inhibition. To understand these processes more fully, we must study the action of the simplest element of the nervous system: the single neuron.

Neurons come in many shapes and sizes, as shown in Figure 3-1. They all possess a cell body (called the soma) and two types of fiber processes: Dendrites, which receive stimulation (directly, or from receptors, or from

34

3

other nerve cells) are short, tapered, multibranched, and unmyelinated; and axons, which typically conduct nerve impulses rapidly over long distances, are usually long, uniform in diameter, and often covered with a fatty layer (myelin). The axon (the impulse conductor) may arise from any response-generator structure, whether transducing receptor terminals, or synapse-bearing surfaces (dendrites, cell-body surface, or axon hillock). At their destination, axons split into small terminals called telodendria. These are involved in transmission of the impulse across the next synapse. The cell body, upon which many axons synapse, is, in addition, concerned with the metabolic and growth functions of the nerve cell. If a nerve fiber is cut, the cell body can often grow a new fiber, particularly if the damage occurs in the periph-eral part of the nervous system (outside the bony covering provided by the skull and spinal vertebrae) where the fibers are covered by a nerve sheath called the neurilemma. If the cell body is damaged, however, the whole neuron dies. If an axon is cut away from its cell body, it is still able to conduct normal nerve impulses for many hours. Thus, the variables necessary for the production and transmission of nerve impulses are still present in the isolated axon. For purposes of conceptualization, we may therefore view the fiber processes as being concerned with the generation and transmission of nerve impulses, and the translation of these impulses into effects on other neurons, or on response-producing cells like muscles or glands. Let us examine the axon more closely.

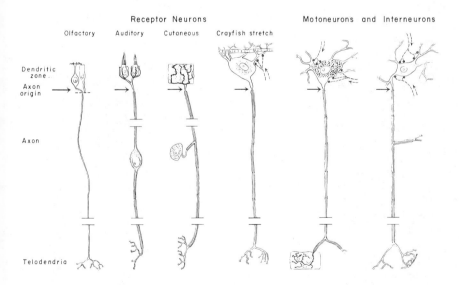

Figure 3-1 Diagram of a variety of receptor and effector neurons. Each part of a neuron may be understood in terms of the function it performs— namely, response-generation (dendrites, cell-body surface, or axon origin), conduction (the axon), and synaptic transmission (telodendria). The interior of the cell body is believed to function mainly in growth and metabolism of the cell. (D. Bodian. Science, 1962, 137, 323–326.)

For our study, we choose the giant axon of the squid, discovered by the British zoologist J. Z. Young to be 0.5-1 millimeter in diameter. Its large size makes it much easier to study than even the largest (one-fiftieth of a millimeter in diameter) mammalian nerve fibers. The axon consists of protoplasm (the axoplasm) enclosed in the cell membrane. If the axoplasm is squeezed out and replaced with a solution containing an appropriate concentration of potassium salts, the axon still generates normal nerve impulses. Therefore, axoplasm is not essential. In appropriate solutions, the membrane alone can produce the nerve impulse.

THE RESTING MEMBRANE

The squid axon (Figure 3-2) is large enough that a fine microelectrode can be inserted into one end and pushed along inside it for several centimeters without affecting its normal activity. Another electrode is then placed on the outside surface of the axon membrane, and both electrodes are connected to a sensitive galvanometer or to an oscilloscope. It is found that current flows from the outside electrode, through the galvanometer, to the inside of the axon. Since current flows from plus to minus, the outside of the axon membrane is positive with respect to its inside surface. The difference in potential is found to be about 50-70 mv (millivolts). This measurement, first performed in 1940 by two British neurophysiologists, Howard J. Curtis and Kenneth S. Cole, is a modern version of experiments carried out by Emil du Bois-Reymond, years earlier, in 1848. He noticed that when a muscle is cut, an injury current flows from the outside surface to the cut (inside) surface. Also, if the muscle is stimulated, the current of injury drops to little or nothing when the wave of muscular contraction passes beneath the outside electrode. From these and other results, Julius Bernstein later reasoned that the membrane in its normal state is polarized (outside positive, inside negative) and that the action potential in all

Figure 3-2 Photomicrograph of a recording electrode inside a giant axon of a squid. The giant axon, which shows as a clear space, was left with small nerve fibers on either side. One scale division is equal to 33 μ. (A. L. Hodgkin and A. F. Huxley. Nature (London), 1939, 144, 710– 711.)

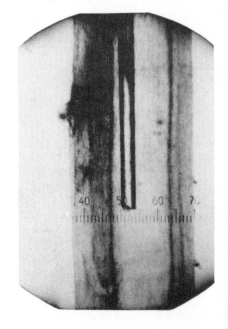

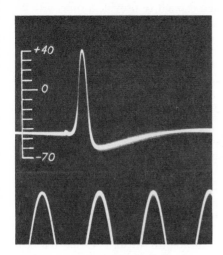

Figure 3-3   Resting and action potential of a giant nerve fiber of a squid recorded directly between the sea-water outside (taken as zero) and a fine wire passed down the axis cylinder. For this particular preparation, the resting potential is −45 mv, and the action potential (from −45 to +40 mv) is 85 mv. There is an interval of 2 milliseconds between successive peaks of the time tracing. (A. L. Hodgkin and A. F. Huxley. Nature (London), 1939, 144, 710–711.)

nervous tissue is a brief passive wave of depolarization which is conducted along the membrane. Immediately after each impulse, the membrane repolarizes and is ready to conduct the next impulse. This is Bernstein's Membrane Theory of Nervous Conduction, formulated in 1902.

If we measure the concentration of potassium ions in the axoplasm inside a squid nerve fiber relative to that in the body fluids which normally bathe it (or in sea water, which is quite similar), we find many more potassium ions inside the fiber. The concentration difference is enough to produce a difference in potential of 50-70 mv. Furthermore, if we decrease the potassium ion concentration difference (by adding potassium ions to the fluid outside the fiber), the resting potential decreases accordingly. Conversely, adding potassium to the inside increases the resting potential. Therefore, the resting potential is related to the unequal concentrations of potassium ions inside and outside the cell membrane.

THE ACTION POTENTIAL

On the basis of Bernstein's membrane theory of nervous conduction, as a nerve impulse passes under the electrode, the difference in potential should first fall to zero as the membrane is depolarized, and then return to its original state as the membrane is repolarized. However, as shown in Figure 3-3, a startling fact was discovered by Curtis and Cole: The conducted action potential actually causes the inside of the membrane to reverse its polarity, to become positive by as much as 40-50 mv. The total change of potential can be as much as 120 mv, much larger than the resting membrane potential of 50-70 mv. Therefore, the resting membrane potential alone cannot produce the nerve impulse. There must be another source of energy. We know that the isolated axon in sea water will conduct impulses normally, even if the axoplasm has been replaced by a potassium sulfate solution of proper concentration.

The Neuron
and
the Synapse

If we measure the concentration of sodium ions in the sea water bathing the outside of the fiber, we find it just high enough to provide a difference in potential of 120 mv. Therefore, the sodium-concentration difference across the cell membrane probably provides the energy for the action potential. If we decrease the concentration of sodium in the external solution, we find, as one would expect, that the height of the action potential decreases. Experiments such as these support the membrane theory in that the immediate source of energy for the production of nerve impulses is provided by the ionic-concentration gradients across the membrane. But the modern version of the theory is modified: The resting potential is related to the concentration of potassium ions and the action potential to that of sodium ions.

By radioactively tagging the ions surrounding the nerve fiber, we can measure the degree to which sodium and potassium ions move into or out of the nerve fiber. Clearly, potassium is highly concentrated inside the nerve fiber. Does it stay there because the membrane does not permit it to move out? No, for if we place tagged potassium ions in the solution outside the fiber, we find that they rapidly move across the membrane and enter the cell. But the nerve membrane is not freely permeable to all ions. Inside the cell are negatively charged protein ions, too large to cross the membrane. The potassium ions which could otherwise freely cross the membrane are kept inside to counteract the negative charge of the protein ions. The potassium concentration difference thus established produces the resting membrane potential.

The inside of the fiber contains very few sodium ions. Since they are highly concentrated in the external fluid, they should tend to enter the cell, not only because of the concentration gradient but because of the same electrical pull (exerted by the protein ions) which keeps the potassium inside. Therefore the membrane must be highly impermeable to sodium, or else the fiber must pump sodium out as fast as it enters. Again, by radioactive tagging, we see that some sodium does leak in (though not as readily as potassium), but the fiber pumps it out very rapidly. The energy for this "sodium pump" is provided by the metabolism of the nerve cell.

During the action potential, the membrane becomes highly permeable (we know this because its electrical resistance drops), and sodium ions rush in, in such quantity as to reverse the polarity of the inside of the fiber at that point, making it as much as 40-50 mv positive with respect to the outside of the fiber. Thus, the 70 mv resting potential of the nerve membrane (provided by the potassium ion concentration difference) acts like a hair trigger on a gun. The energy required to trip that trigger (excite the fiber) is small, but it releases a more powerful charge (the 120 mv action potential provided by the sodium ion concentration difference).

THE LOCAL CIRCUIT THEORY
OF CONDUCTION OF THE NERVE IMPULSE

It had long been known that nerves are easily excited by weak electric shocks and that they can be repeatedly stimulated electrically without any sign of nerve damage. In addition, it was known that an electrical impulse,

Figure 3-4 The local circuit theory of nerve conduction. The upper drawing represents an unmyelinated nerve fiber, the lower one illustrates saltatory conduction between nodes of Ranvier in a myelinated nerve fiber. (A. L. Hodgkin. The Conduction of the Nerve Impulse. Springfield: C. C. Thomas, 1964, p. 32.)

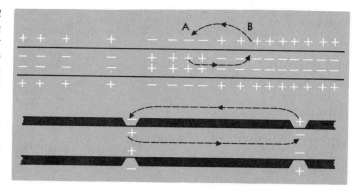

corresponding to the nerve impulse, passes down the nerve. It was therefore reasonable to assume (as has since been proven by many experiments) that each nerve impulse electrically excites the area of nerve ahead of it, thus causing it to move along the fiber, in a manner analogous to the way a burning fuse ignites each area just ahead. According to this theory, originally formulated by Bernstein (and now modified to include sodium ions), propagation of the nerve impulse is brought about by a flow of current between resting and active nerve. Consider the top part of Figure 3-4, which is an example of current flow in an unmyelinated fiber, such as the squid axon. The action potential is at point A, and B is the area of the resting nerve just ahead. The outside of the fiber at B is positive (permeable to potassium) but, in the active area at A, the outside is negative (sodium ions are rushing in). Electric current flows in a local circuit from B to A outside the fiber, and from A to B inside the fiber. As positive charge flows from B, the outside surface of the nerve membrane loses its positive charge (becomes increasingly depolarized), thereby increasing its permeability to sodium ions. With sufficient depolarization, a point is reached (threshold) when sodium ions suddenly rush in, initiating the action potential at that point, and setting up the same type of local electrical circuit between B and the point ahead of it. So we see that the action potential is a wave of internal positivity (increased sodium permeability) which passes along the nerve fiber. The local electric current is produced by the change in permeability. (If an action potential were initiated by an electric shock at point A, we see in Figure 3-4 (top) that current should also flow from points behind A, just as it does from B, ahead of A. The region behind A should also become depolarized. Therefore an impulse initiated in the middle of a fiber should travel in both directions away from the stimulus. This is exactly what happens. If the nerve impulse has been traveling down the fiber, then the area behind is temporarily refractory to stimulation, so the nerve impulse only travels forward.)

Vertebrate nerve fibers are usually covered with myelin, a fatty sheath which acts like an insulator. In such fibers, the membrane is exposed at regularly spaced intervals. These bare areas are called nodes of Ranvier.

As shown at the bottom of Figure 3-4, the local current set up by an action potential flows between adjacent nodes, producing depolarization at each node. Conduction in myelinated fibers is saltatory—the nerve impulse jumps from one node to the next—making for faster conduction than in an unmyelinated fiber of the same diameter.

A negatively charged electrode (cathode) applied to the outside of a fiber neutralizes the excess of positively charged ions there. If sufficient depolarization occurs, a self-propagated action potential is set up, which then travels along the fiber. If, however, the current is cut off before the threshold for generating the action potential is reached, the local changes in membrane polarization are dissipated gradually. A second stimulus applied at the same point, before the depolarization has decayed, will excite the nerve more easily. The effectiveness of the second stimulus is facilitated by the traces of the previous one. This is the basis for temporal summation. A pile of sand being poured upon a flat surface spreads out as it builds up. So, too, does the depolarization produced locally on the nerve membrane. This is the basis for spatial summation. A subthreshold stimulus, applied nearby, requires less intensity to excite the fiber, because the depolarization it produces sums with that produced by the adjacent stimulus.

If the depolarizing current flow is maintained, the depolarization builds up to a point and then drops down to a lower level. In the nerve fiber, this decrement in the effectiveness of a maintained stimulus is called accommodation. It is analogous to sensory adaptation in a receptor exposed to a maintained stimulus. When the stimulus is terminated, the membrane shows a compensatory increase in polarization. This rebound indicates that accommodation is caused by an antagonistic process (still poorly understood) in the nerve membrane that actively combats the depolarizing effect of the stimulus. Accommodation is the reason that every stimulus has a threshold (an intensity below which it is unable to excite). If the effect of a stimulus cumulated indefinitely, any stimulus, no matter how weak, would become effective if maintained long enough. But because of accommodation, energy change must be rapid to excite.

Underneath the anode, the positively charged electrode, exactly the opposite events occur. The excess of positive charge hyperpolarizes the membrane, making it more difficult to initiate a nerve impulse there (inhibition). Thus, a nerve impulse can be blocked by local hyperpolarization produced by a positive electrode (anodal block).

We can now understand the way a stimulus is coded into a transmitted message in the nervous system. Receptors are structures specially differentiated to transform physical energy of various forms (light, heat, pressure, movement, chemical energy) into changes in the resting membrane potential of their nerve fibers. As shown in Figure 3-5, the stimulus produces in the receptor a depolarizing potential (the generator potential) whose amplitude increases with the intensity of the stimulus. The greater the amount of depolarization, the higher the frequency of nerve impulses produced. Although the local nonpropagated generator potential can grow larger and larger with the intensity of the stimulus (graded response),

The Neuron
and
the Synapse

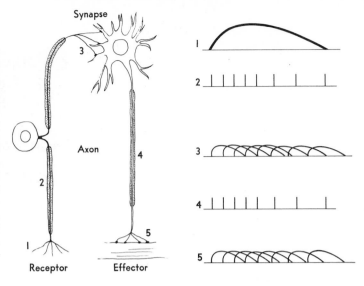

Figure 3-5 Diagram of a simple sensorimotor neuronal circuit. At the right, potentials developed by the neuronal activity at: (1) the receptor; (2) the axon; (3) the synapse; (4) the axon; (5) the effector. (E. de Robertis. Histophysiology of Synapses and Neurosecretion. *Oxford: Pergamon Press, 1964. As modified from* G. H. Bishop. Physiol. Rev., *1956, 36, 376–399.)

Synapse

3

Axon

2

1

Receptor

4

5

Effector

1

2

3

4

5

the axon membrane must repolarize after each all-or-none action potential. Therefore, the rate of firing in an axon is limited by the duration of time the membrane is completely refractory, that is, unresponsive. The shortest absolute refractory period in any nerve fiber is about 0.5-1 m sec, and so 1000-2000 impulses per second is the highest rate at which any fiber could possibly fire. In actuality, the nerve is still relatively refractory to conduction for several milliseconds, so most nerves fire well below the theoretical limit, usually no higher than 300 per second.

At the other end of the neuron, the axon usually branches into a number of small fibers which synapse with another neuron or a muscle or gland cell. Each nerve impulse produces a local change in the postsynaptic membrane potential in a way analogous to the receptor potentials initiated by the original stimulus. Excitatory nerve endings depolarize the membrane of the cell they end on, inhibitory endings hyperpolarize it. The graded net effect on the postsynaptic cell will determine the pattern of firing generated in it.

We see in Figure 3-5 that graded potentials are set up by receptors and converted into all-or-none signals conducted by the axon, which in turn converts them back into graded potentials on the next neuron, muscle, or gland. According to this view, the axon is simply a structure specialized through evolution for high-speed accurate communication over long distances.

THE SYNAPSE

At about the time that anatomical techniques were beginning to provide support for the theory that the nervous system is made up of closely contiguous, but separate, neurons, physiological evidence was also mounting which indicated that the synapse, the point of contact between two neurons, has properties different from the nerve fibers themselves. Thus, electrical stimulation of a nerve fiber sets up nerve impulses that travel away from the point of stimulation in both directions along the nerve. Stimulation across a synapse, however, occurs in only one direction; like a valve, the synapse allows only forward conduction in the nervous system. If a nerve fiber is stimulated repeatedly, it will eventually become fatigued, that is, unable to conduct further stimulation until allowed to rest for a period of time. The synapse is much more prone to fatigue: Conduction across a synapse fails long before the individual fibers stop firing in response to repeated stimulation. Asphyxia and a variety of drugs also affect the synapse before the nerve fiber is affected. Curare, for instance, blocks conduction across a nerve-muscle junction without affecting the excitability of the nerve or muscle.

There has been a good deal of controversy over the nature of synaptic transmission—is it chemical or electrical? For many years

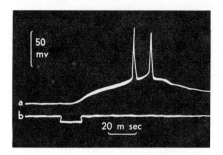

Figure 3-6 External application of acetylcholine to a motor end-plate. An ACh-filled micropipette was placed on the outside of an end-plate, and a quantity of ACh was released by passing a brief outward-directed current pulse through the pipette (registered in b). It produced the effect shown in trace a: a depolarization developing after a diffusion delay and culminating in two action potentials. (J. del Castillo and B. Katz. J. Physiol., 1955, 128, 157–181.)

it seemed simpler to assume that electrical current-flow set up by an impulse in the pre-synaptic fiber directly depolarized the membrane of the dendrite or cell body of the postsynaptic cell. However, a great deal of evidence now suggests that a chemical transmitter is usually necessary for synaptic conduction. Micropipette studies of the neuromuscular junction indicate that acetylcholine is essential for depolarization of the motor end-plate, the receptive subsynaptic surface of a muscle. Electrical stimulation, no matter how strong, does not depolarize the motor end-plate; injection of tiny quantities of acetylcholine into the synaptic space outside the membrane easily depolarizes it and generates nerve impulses (Figure 3-6).

In 1954, the electron microscope, with a resolving power of 10 Ångström units, was used to study the fine structure of the nervous system. For the first time it became possible to see the nerve-cell membranes and the structural details of synapses. Many nerve fibers end on the cell body and dendrites of a neuron. These synapses are often recognizable under the light microscope by the swollen endings (terminal boutons) of the presynaptic cells. Under the electron microscope, as shown diagrammatically in Figure 3-7, these boutons are found to be packed with synaptic vesicles, tiny droplets of chemicals formed by the presynaptic neuron at its terminals. When stimulated, the neuron discharges many of these vesicles into the synaptic cleft where they act to change the permeability of the subsynaptic surface of the adjacent neuron. Excitatory synapses depolarize, and inhibitory synapses hyper-

The Neuron
and
the Synapse

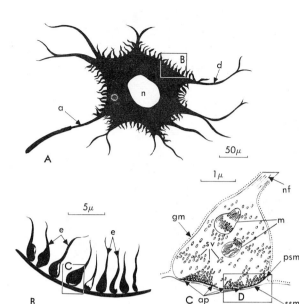

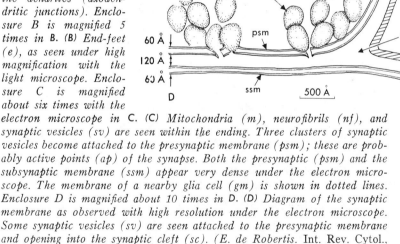

Figure 3-7   Diagram showing bouton-like synaptic junctions as they appear at different magnifications with the optical and electron microscope. (A) The nucleus (n), the axon (a), and the dendrites (d) are indicated. The terminal boutons make synaptic contact with the surface of the cell body (axosomatic junctions) and of the dendrites (axodendritic junctions). Enclosure B is magnified 5 times in B. (B) End-feet (e), as seen under high magnification with the light microscope. Enclosure C is magnified about six times with the electron microscope in C. (C) Mitochondria (m), neurofibrils (nf), and synaptic vesicles (sv) are seen within the ending. Three clusters of synaptic vesicles become attached to the presynaptic membrane (psm); these are probably active points (ap) of the synapse. Both the presynaptic (psm) and the subsynaptic membrane (ssm) appear very dense under the electron microscope. The membrane of a nearby glia cell (gm) is shown in dotted lines. Enclosure D is magnified about 10 times in D. (D) Diagram of the synaptic membrane as observed with high resolution under the electron microscope. Some synaptic vesicles (sv) are seen attached to the presynaptic membrane and opening into the synaptic cleft (sc). (E. de Robertis. Int. Rev. Cytol., 1959, 8, 61–96.)

polarize, the membrane of the postsynaptic cell. Acetylcholine is the chemical transmitter found at nerve muscle junctions and at many neuronal synapses, but noradrenalin and other neural transmitters have also been found. Therefore, although there is some evidence of purely electrical synapses, particularly in invertebrates, it is currently believed that synaptic conduction is typically chemical in nature.

The Neuron
and
the Synapse

Stimulus-Intensity Coding
in the Nervous System

We have seen that several psychophysical laws of human vision can be reduced directly to the activity of simple elements of the visual system. Thus, the Bunsen-Roscoe law, $IT = C$ is observed in the action of a single crab receptor; and Ricco's law, $IA = C$, in a single ganglion cell in the cat retina. Visual contrast phenomena such as Mach bands appear in the purely inhibitory interaction of crab photoreceptors.

Further analysis reduces such phenomena of excitation and inhibition to corresponding changes in the membrane polarization of each neuron. Depolarization excites, hyperpolarization inhibits; in response to environmental

44

4

stimuli, receptors set up local generator potentials which in turn produce propagated action potentials. The stronger the stimulus, the greater the frequency of identical nerve impulses generated in a given nerve fiber, and the greater the number of fibers responding to the stimulus. Via a chemical transmitter, the process is continued across the synapse to other neurons, and eventually, to muscles or glands.

After analysis, synthesis. Given these facts, can we now explain the character of the psychological sensations produced by stimuli? For instance, does our knowledge of the pattern of increase in firing in a single fiber help us to account for the psychologically perceived increase in the intensity of sensation? Or is there more we need to know about how the nervous system processes the information contained in sensory stimuli?

As mentioned earlier (pp. 9–11), a mathematical model is a form of synthesis. On the basis of a theoretical analysis, we can isolate hypothetical units and mathematically predict their function in a set of equations. For instance, consider the problem of stimulus-intensity coding. Long before it was known that nerve fibers signaled an increase in intensity of stimulation by an increase in frequency of nerve impulses, advances in the physical measurement of stimulus energy made it possible to ask: How does the psychological intensity of a sensation vary with the change in intensity of a physical stimulus? Does a light seem twice as bright when we double its physical energy? Is a sound twice as loud? But how can we measure psychological intensity? How can we assign a number to a given psychological intensity when we don't even know how much one unit is?

In 1850, Gustav Fechner had an idea which was to become the basis of much of modern psychophysics. If a change in physical intensity is too small, we cannot detect it. The difference in stimulus intensity which is just noticeable must equal the smallest increase (the unit) of sensation magnitude. A little thought, however, reveals a difficulty with this definition. To be just noticeable, a change in a large intensity must be much greater than a change in a smaller intensity. When we have only one candle in a room, we easily perceive the increased brightness added by another candle; if 200 candles are lit, adding one more makes no noticeable difference. Fechner solved this problem by using some earlier observations of Ernst Heinrich Weber. While studying people's ability to discriminate changes in intensity of stimulation, Weber found that a just noticeable addition to the intensity of stimulation (ΔI) represented a constant fraction of the total level of stimulation (I) produced. For example, a just noticeable difference (j.n.d.) in brightness was produced when one candle was added to 63 ($\Delta I/I = \frac{1}{64}$), two candles to 126, and so on. Although the Weber fraction was different for each modality ($\frac{1}{10}$ for loudness, $\frac{1}{30}$ for weight, and so forth), it was believed to be constant over a large part of the normal range of perceived intensity in each modality.

Stimulus-
Intensity
Coding

Given that $\Delta I / I$ is constant, Fechner realized that, by making two simple assumptions, he could derive a general mathematical formula to describe the growth of psychological sensation (S) in relation to the increase in intensity of the physical stimulus (I). First he assumed that at any level of stimulus intensity the psychological magnitude of a just noticeable difference is always the same. That is, any j.n.d. $= \Delta S = \Delta I / I$, a unit of sensation. Second, in order to be able to perform the mathematical processes of differentiation and integration, he assumed that ΔS and ΔI could become infinitely small. In mathematical terms, a j.n.d. $= dS = dI / I$. To calculate the total psychological intensity of sensation (S), one need merely add up (integrate) all the j.n.d.'s in sensation from the absolute threshold to the particular level in question. Integrating both sides of the equation, we find that S (the integral of dS) is proportional to log I (the integral of dI / I). In other words, psychological sensation grows as the logarithm of physical intensity. Intuitively, one can formulate the same law: To add a unit of sensation, one must multiply the stimulus energy by a constant amount. Sensation grows arithmetically when the stimulus grows geometrically. That is what a logarithm means: Equal additions on one scale are equivalent to equal ratios on another.

Physiological Correlates
of Fechner's Law

When the technique of electrophysiological recording became available, it was immediately possible to ask whether the frequency of firing in a single nerve fiber (the physiological correlate of the intensity of sensation) shows the same logarithmic relation to the intensity of physical stimulation.

Bryan Matthews in Adrian's laboratory added weights to the isolated toe muscle of a frog, and recorded the rate of firing in a single fiber stimulated by a stretch receptor in that muscle. Figure 4-1 shows that the frequency of firing can be fitted by a logarithmic function. Similarly, as mentioned earlier, H. K. Hartline and C. H. Graham, using the *Limulus* eye, found that the rate of firing in a single optic nerve fiber increased in response to the increased intensity of light. A logarithmic function such as curve A in Figure 4-2 is a pretty good fit to these data. And so, for a hundred

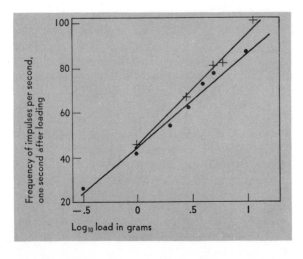

Figure 4-1   Discharge of a frog muscle spindle under different loads. The graph shows the relationship of the frequency 1 second after loading to the logarithm of the load. Temperature 15° C. (B. H. C. Matthews. J. Physiol., 1931, 71, 64–110.)

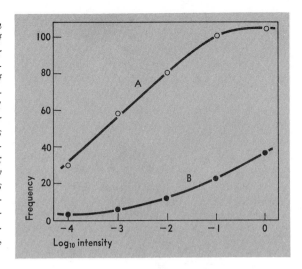

Figure 4-2 The relation between frequency of impulses (number per second) and the logarithm of the intensity of stimulating light. Intensity in arbitrary units (1 unit = 630,000 meter candles). Curve A shows the frequency of the initial maximal discharge; curve B, the frequency of discharge 3.5 seconds after the onset of illumination. (H. K. Hartline and C. H. Graham. J. cell. comp. Physiol., 1932, 1, 277–295.)

years, Fechner's law has been accepted as the best formula relating psychological sensation to physical intensity.

STEVENS' POWER LAW: $S = kI^n$

S. S. Stevens, a sensory psychologist at Harvard University, recently has challenged the validity of Fechner's law. His argument, simply stated, is this: Fechner's law is not based on a direct measure of the intensity of psychological sensation. It measures error, not magnitude. The resolving power of the nervous system is not a valid measure of its output at any level of stimulation. In addition, he claims that Fechner was wrong in assuming that there is a constant unit increment in sensation—actually, the psychological magnitude of a j.n.d. at a high intensity is greater than that of a j.n.d. produced at a low intensity. Therefore, Fechner was not justified in adding them up to produce an indirect estimate of sensation magnitude. Stevens takes a direct approach: He presents a subject with a standard tone, for instance, and tells him to call that intensity 10. Then he presents another tone. If it sounds twice as loud, the subject is to call it 20; 10 times as loud is called 100; one-half as loud is called 5, and so on. The subject estimates the ratio of the sensation produced by each stimulus to that produced by the standard. When subjects use this technique (which Stevens calls the method of magnitude estimation), they usually generate a function that is best fit by a curve of the form $S = kI^n$, which says that the sensation magnitude is proportional to stimulus intensity raised to a certain power. For every modality tested so far (light, sound, weight, taste, smell, pain of electric shock), a power function rather than a logarithmic relationship has been found, although the exponent, n, is different for each sense modality. Brightness of light, for example, has an exponent of 0.33; painfulness of electric shock, 1.6.

Stimulus-
Intensity
Coding

These findings fit our everyday experience. The painfulness of electric shock rises very sharply in response to a relatively small increase in shock intensity, whereas a tenfold increase in the intensity of light is needed to make it seem twice as bright. The visual system compresses a tremendous range of light

Figure 4-3 Some reflex connections in the spinal cord. Motor neurons (whose cell bodies are in the ventral horns of the butterfly-shaped gray matter) can be influenced by both proprioceptive and exteroceptive (common sensibility) fibers. Proprioceptive fibers send a branch directly to extensor motor neurons at their level of entrance. They also have ascending and descending collateral branches which act via an interneuron to inhibit antagonistic flexor neurons at levels above and below in the spinal cord. The net result is that proprioceptive impulses usually cause extensor reflexes (such as the knee-jerk). Exteroceptive, particularly painful impulses synapse with cells in the dorsal horn, which in turn end on flexor motor neurons, yielding flexor reflexes, such as leg withdrawal. (Copyright The Ciba Collection of Medical Illustrations *by Frank H. Netter, M.D.* Vol. I, Nervous System. *Summit, N.J.: 1953.)*

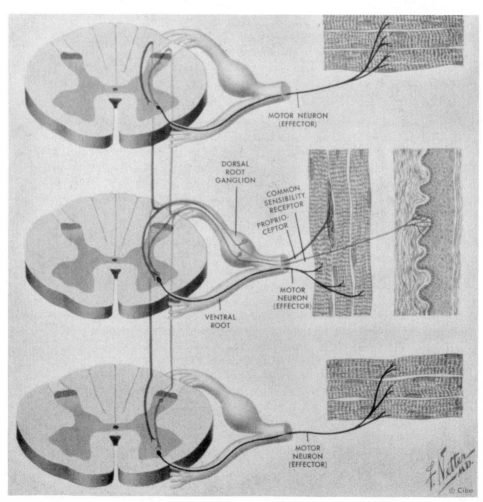

intensity, whereas pain expands the harmful change in noxious stimulus intensity, prompting us to move away before our tissue is damaged.

Physiological Correlates
of Stevens' Power Law

Stevens' power law has recently received striking confirmation from physiological work on monkeys. Vernon Mountcastle and his co-workers at The Johns Hopkins University have been studying the proprioceptive (also called kinesthetic) system—the sensory system which enables us to discriminate the position of our arms and legs in space and to sense their movements without looking at them. As shown in Figures 4-3 and 4-4, receptors in our muscles and joints are stimulated when the muscles stretch or contract, or when the limbs are moved. Impulses from these receptors are carried by sensory nerve fibers in peripheral nerves via the dorsal spinal roots into the spinal cord. Some of them, such as those detecting muscle stretch, are involved in automatic reflex postural adjustments. As shown in Figure 4-3, these fibers often end on motor neurons in the ventral part of the cord at the same level of the spinal cord which they enter. Those nerve fibers involved in our conscious awareness of muscles and joints (see Figure 4-4) enter the spinal cord and run up toward the brain in a bundle of fibers, called the dorsal spinal column. They end on clusters of nerve cells (nuclei) in the medulla. These second-order neurons, in turn, send fibers into the medial lemniscus, a pathway which crosses over to the opposite side in the brain stem and proceeds upwards to end on third-order neurons clustered in the thalamus, which project in turn to the sensory areas of the cortex of the brain.

The cells in the thalamus that mediate the last well-known link in the transformation of raw stimuli to conscious sensations were the ones Mountcastle and his group chose to study. An instrument was devised by which a monkey's arm or leg could be gripped and subjected to precisely measurable amounts and rates of angular rotation. Then, with a microelectrode, the investigators probed the brain until they located a thalamic cell which responded to leg rotation, signaled by the firing of a joint receptor.

But they had to be sure that these cells were actually involved in conscious discrimination. If they used anesthetized monkeys, the cells which responded actively when the animal was unconscious might not be the ones used when the animal was conscious, or the pattern of their activity in response to stimulation might be changed under anesthesia. So a procedure was developed which allowed them to record from the brain of the waking animal. The head of a conscious monkey was fixed firmly in a stereotaxic instrument. To eliminate any possible pain from this procedure, a deafferented head preparation was developed: in a previous operation, all the sensory nerves leading from the skin of the face and head were cut. At the same time, an assembly was implanted on the monkey's skull which allowed the experimenters to introduce the tiny microelectrode into the monkey's brain. After the animal had recovered, they could take it out of its cage any time they wished, fix its head in the stereotaxic instrument, and explore its brain with the moveable microelectrode attached to the recording system. The micro-

Stimulus-
Intensity
Coding

49

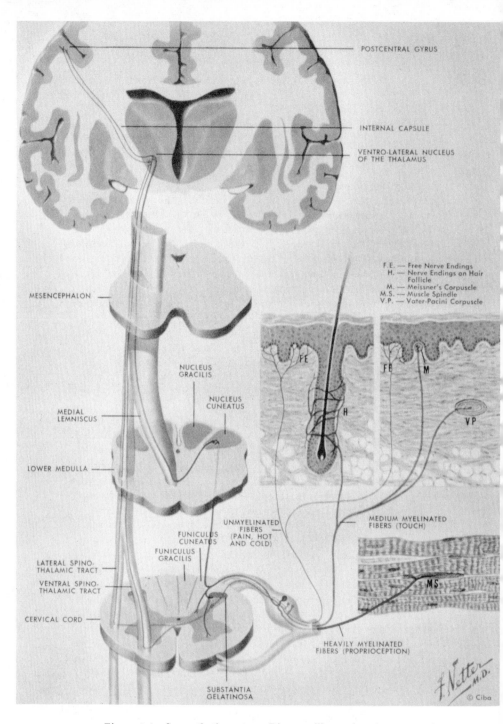

POSTCENTRAL GYRUS

INTERNAL CAPSULE

VENTRO-LATERAL NUCLEUS
OF THE THALAMUS

F.E. — Free Nerve Endings
H. — Nerve Endings on Hair
Follicle
M. — Meissner's Corpuscle
M.S. — Muscle Spindle
V.P. — Vater-Pacini Corpuscle

MESENCEPHALON

NUCLEUS
GRACILIS

NUCLEUS
CUNEATUS

MEDIAL
LEMNISCUS

LOWER MEDULLA

MEDIUM MYELINATED
FIBERS (TOUCH)

UNMYELINATED
FIBERS
(PAIN, HOT
AND COLD)

FUNICULUS
CUNEATUS

FUNICULUS
GRACILIS

LATERAL SPINO-
THALAMIC TRACT

VENTRAL SPINO-
THALAMIC TRACT

CERVICAL CORD

MS

HEAVILY MYELINATED
FIBERS (PROPRIOCEPTION)

SUBSTANTIA
GELATINOSA

F. Netter
M.D.

© Ciba

*Figure 4-4 Somesthetic system. Diagram illustrating the course of exterocep-
tive (from the skin) or proprioceptive (from muscles, tendons, and joints)
fibers into the spinal cord and up to the brain. Proprioceptive fibers ascend
in the dorsal columns of the spinal cord and end on cells in the medulla.
These cross over and ascend in the medial lemniscus to end on cells in the
thalamus. These in turn project to the sensory cortex. Some exteroceptive*

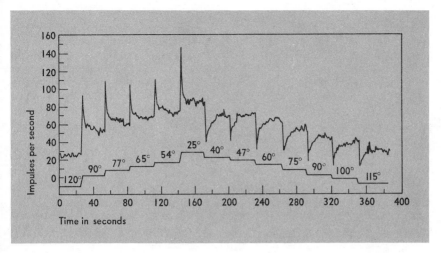

Figure 4-5   Response of a thalamic neuron sensitive to flexion of the contra-lateral knee joint. The graph plots impulses per second as a function of time. Starting from an open position (angle of 120°), the knee is flexed, first to 90°, 77°, 65°, etc. From a maximally closed position (25° angle), the knee is opened again in steps to 115°. (V. B. Mountcastle, G. F. Poggio, and G. Werner. J. Neurophysiol, *1963, 26, 807–834.)*

electrode had little or no effect on the monkey, who lived normally in the animal colony between experiments.

The experimenters started with the limb in a flexed position and recorded the resting level of activity of the thalamic cell. Then they moved the limb and recorded the change in the cell's activity. This was done repeatedly, varying the amount and speed of rotation of the joint. Some cells increased their activity in response to joint extension and decreased it when the joint was flexed. Others were opposite in type; more active in response to flexion, less in response to extension; but all cells had the same general response to change. When the joint was moved, a rapid burst of firing occurred which quickly adapted to a lower steady state (Figure 4-5). The greater the amount of rotation, the greater the change in the level of firing. For any given cell, a minimum (threshold) amount of joint rotation was necessary to produce a change in firing.

If Fechner's law holds for a given thalamic cell, then as the angle of joint rotation is increased past threshold, the rate of firing of that cell should increase arithmetically as the angle of rotation is increased geometrically—the firing rate should be proportional to the logarithm of the angle of joint rotation. As shown in Figure 4-6, Mountcastle found that the steady-state

fibers (large and rapidly conducting) also ascend in the dorsal columns of the same side. But many (small, unmyelinated) synapse on cells in the dorsal horn. These then cross at the level of entry in the cord and ascend in the ventral (touch) and lateral (pain and temperature) spinothalamic tracts. (Copyright The Ciba Collection of Medical Illustrations *by Frank H. Netter, M.D.* Vol. I, Nervous System. *Summit, N.J.: 1953.)*

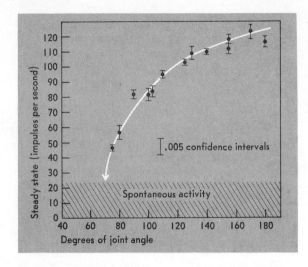

Figure 4-6 Response of a thalamic neuron driven by extension of the contralateral knee joint. The graph plots frequency of firing in the steady state as a function of knee-joint angle. The intercept of the fitted curve with the spontaneous activity level of the neuron is defined as the threshold of excitatory angle for the cell. (V. B. Mountcastle, G. F. Poggio, and G. Werner. J. Neurophysiol., *1963, 26, 807–834.)*

firing rate increased as a power function of the rotational stimulus: Steady-state firing rate $= kS^n$. The exponent, which is close to 1.0, approximates that described by Stevens for the psychological magnitude-estimation of lifted weights. Thus, the physiological response of a thalamic cell to joint rotation supports the view that psychological intensity of sensation varies as a power function of the intensity of the stimulus.

Does this mean that the earlier physiological results of Adrian and Matthews and of Hartline and Graham were wrong? Not necessarily. It is possible that the initial burst of firing of first-order neurons in sensory nerves is a logarithmic function of intensity, but that the later steady-state rate (see Figure 4-2, curve labeled B) is a power function. Also, at successive synapses, additional transformations of the stimulus may occur in the central nervous system. Perhaps, by the time the third-order neurons in the thalamus react, they do so as a power function of stimulus intensity. Obviously, the next step is to determine whether the activity of first-order neurons involved in joint rotation is a power function of rotation. Also, the earlier experiments should be repeated with the improved techniques now available. Clearly, we are only beginning to understand the kinds of synaptic transformations performed at different levels of the nervous system and their relations to psychological experience.

The Analysis
of Behavior

As I have repeatedly pointed out, to understand behavior we must break it down into simpler units, then learn how these units combine to produce that behavior. What are the units of behavior?

About 150 years ago, Pierre Flourens, one of the great early French physiologists, attacked this problem in a classically simple way. By cutting at various levels, and by removing entire parts, he completely separated the lower portions of the nervous system from the influence of higher parts. He then studied the behavior which remained.

53

5

For instance, Flourens determined the effect on a pigeon of the removal of both cerebral lobes. The pigeon stood erect very well; when placed on its back it righted itself; it maintained its equilibrium, and if disturbed did not rest until it had regained equilibrium. When pushed, it walked; when thrown into the air, it flew. The irises of both its eyes responded appropriately to light (sensation), and yet it did not see (perception); it did not hear, or move spontaneously, and often resembled a sleeping or unconscious animal. When water was placed in its beak, it swallowed; when annoyed, it moved away from the source of irritation. When left to itself, however, it remained calm, showing no sign of voluntary action or desire. One could prick it, pinch it, burn it—it moved, became disturbed, and walked away, but never far; it no longer appeared to know enough to flee. If it encountered an obstacle, it bumped into it, and returned to bump again and again, without ever seeking to avoid it.

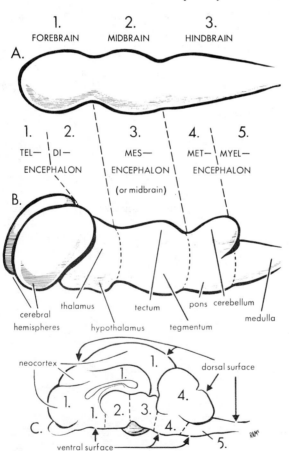

Figure 5-1 Embryonic pattern of development for the vertebrate brain. (A) In the very young embryo, the primitive tubular brain first develops three subdivisions. (B) These three primary subdivisions further subdivide to form five secondary subdivisions: the telencephalon, the diencephalon, the mesencephalon, the metencephalon, and the myelencephalon. Also indicated in B are the areas within these subdivisions where major components of the adult nervous system will further differentiate during subsequent embryonic development. (C) A medial view of the cat brain which has been split lengthwise between the two cerebral hemispheres shows how the five secondary subdivisions came to be distributed in the adult vertebrate brain. In higher vertebrates, such as the cat, a layer of neocortex is also present as the outer shell of the cerebral hemispheres. (R. A. McCleary and R. Y. Moore. Subcortical Mechanisms of Behavior. New York: Basic Books, 1965, p. 19.)

From these results, Flourens concluded that perception, memory, judgment, and volition reside in the cerebral hemispheres. Without them, the pigeon is a reflex machine, reacting automatically to external stimuli, which for an instant, substitute for the spontaneity seen in normal behavior. These automatic reactions are clearly recognizable fragments of normal walking, standing, and avoiding; yet they are simpler, no longer subject to many of the central influences that control them in normal behavior. A reflex is therefore one of the building blocks of behavior.

When the nervous system was cut through the medulla, a pigeon did not survive very long—it breathed irregularly in gasps, and soon stopped breathing or its heart stopped beating. If the cut was made below the medulla in the spinal cord, breathing and heartbeat remained undisturbed. The integrity of the medulla is therefore essential for several vital vegetative reflexes that serve to maintain the internal environment such as breathing, heart rate, and blood pressure.

When the cerebellum alone was removed from the rest of the nervous system, a pigeon appeared able to carry out all its normal movements; it could walk, run, eat, and sleep spontaneously. But it appeared drunk. It lurched as it walked and could hardly keep its balance; when attempting to eat, its peck was wide of the mark, and each successive attempt at correction overshot the food so that the pigeon could hardly get any. Because the behavior of such a decerebellate pigeon appeared to be intact in all its elements, but poorly controlled, Flourens concluded that the role of the cerebellum is to coordinate and control behavioral movements: to smooth, guide, and make them precise.

From such experiments, Flourens drew the important conclusion that there are levels of function in the nervous system: Simpler types of behavior are organized by anatomically lower levels of the nervous system; higher nervous levels superimpose more complex types of control.

Instincts:
Hormonal Control of Reflexes

This classic approach to levels of function has been used again and again in the fruitful study of nervous control of behavior. Sir Charles Scott Sherrington, the great English neurophysiologist, used it at the end of the nineteenth century to study the integration of reflexes in the spinal cord. In the 1930's, Walter B. Cannon in America studied the integration of emotional expression. His associate, Philip Bard, continued this line of work in the study of sexual behavior in the cat. Let us see what Bard did.

About twice a year, when the female cat is in estrous (sexually receptive), it emits a characteristic low, throaty, purring sound, the estrual call. The animal seeks and readily approaches male cats and human beings and rubs its body against them. If its back or genital areas are touched or stroked, the receptive cat will crouch by bending its forelimbs, and tread in place by alternately flexing one hind limb and extending the other. If a glass rod is inserted into its vagina, it will move its tail to one side, and tread very vigorously, while giving the estrual call. If stimulated sufficiently, the cat will reach a violent climax signaled by a loud cry and followed by an after-reaction of rolling and squirming on its back while purring. When not in heat, or if its gonads have been removed, the female cat does not show this behavior. Any stimulation of the genitals in such a cat causes it to move away or display anger.

Bard studied the sexual behavior pattern in spayed female cats whose nervous systems were transected (cut completely through, separating the upper from the lower part) at various levels. In a cat whose spinal cord was separated from the rest of the brain above (hereafter referred to as a spinal cat), even with its gonads removed, stimulation of the genital areas elicited the normal pattern of crouching, tail deflection, and hind-limb treading. Injection with sufficient estrogen to restore sexual behavior in the normal spayed cat made no difference in the spinal cat. The threshold of sexual response to genital stimulation was exactly the same as it was without hormones. If the transection was made at a higher level, in the midbrain above the medulla, the cat still showed no response to hormones; reflex treading, crouching, and tail deflection were still independent of its hormonal state. Only if the transection was above the hypothalamus, allowing the hypothalamus to remain connected to the lower part of the nervous system, did this behavior pattern show any sensitivity to hormonal influence. As in a normal cat, the receptive hypothalamic cat (with only the hypothalamus still connected to the rest of the nervous system below) showed reflex treading, crouching, and tail deflection; but without hormones, it displayed violent rage if its genitals were stimulated. Experiments such as these led to the concept of hypothalamic centers, involved in the integration of hormonal control over reflex patterns mediated by the spinal cord below. Adding only a little bit of tissue (that contained in the hypothalamus) restores hormonal control of sexual behavior. This counterexperiment proves that tissue responsive to hormones exists in the hypothalamus, and that such tissue without any of the brain above is sufficient to exert control over spinal reflexes. Where such a demonstration has been made, one can speak of neural centers of integration. By extrapolation, although such rigorous proof is still lacking, one may think of hypothalamic integration of feeding, drinking, temperature regulation, and so forth.

Motivated Voluntary Behavior

The hypothalamic cat does not seek out sexual stimulation, but its sexual behavior is clearly under hormonal control. As Bard has also shown, a female cat, subjected only to decortication (removal of both cerebral cortexes), is also essentially normal except that, lacking the ability to perceive distant stimuli, it does not respond sexually to distant cats or people that would have ordinarily elicited approach. From Bard's experiments, it is therefore clear that the sexual behavior of the cat is made up of several elements combined into different levels of integration:

(1) *Spinal reflexes*—movement patterns of treading, crouching, and tail deflection that are mediated by the spinal cord and are not sensitive to the level of gonadal hormones in the blood stream.

(2) *Hypothalamic instinctive reactions*—spinal reflex patterns, hormonally controlled by hypothalamic integrating mechanisms. In addition to hormonal

control, the hypothalamus adds an affective component to behavior—the hypothalamic cat shows pleasure or rage when its genitals are stimulated.

(3) *Voluntary motivated behavior*—nonreflexive, self-initiated actions involved in seeking out possible sex objects—these acts indicate a desire to engage in sexual behavior, and are a still higher, more complex level of behavior.

How do we know that the female cat wants to engage in sexual behavior? How can we ever know what an animal wants? When we study animal behavior, we are often struck by its apparent purposiveness. A pin prick to an animal's foot elicits withdrawal, which stops the pain. A grey lag goose, sitting on its nest of eggs will, if one of the eggs rolls out of the nest, reach out and roll it back. A hungry herring-gull chick will peck at its parent's bill, causing the parent bird to feed it by regurgitating food. A hungry rat, after appropriate training, will press a bar to get food.

All these acts produce a desirable outcome—pain is terminated, the egg is restored to the nest, or food is obtained. In trying to explain such behavior, it is tempting to anthropomorphize—to project what we would feel and do in the same situation as a valid description and explanation of the animal's behavior. This is often correct, but it may be attributing more complexity to the behavior than is really there. For example, the pin prick will elicit the same leg withdrawal in an anesthetized animal, or in an animal whose spinal cord has been completely severed, so that pain impulses from the foot cannot possibly get to the brain. The leg withdrawal is a spinal reflex, a built-in fixed response to a painful stimulus. There are no alternatives here. The reflex is a stereotyped automatic response to the stimulus. The grey lag goose will retrieve any egg-shaped object, even a gigantic artificial one. If the egg should happen to slip out from under its bill while being rolled back to the nest, the bird cannot inhibit or correct its movement but must complete the egg-retrieving act, even without the egg. The herring-gull chick will peck at any stimulus when it is hungry, preferably one similar to the parent's beak, which is long and narrow, with a red spot near its tip. The chick will keep on pecking at such an object though no food is obtained from it, and will do so just after being hatched, before it has ever been fed by its parent. Egg-retrieving and bill-pecking should not be classed as purposive acts—they are fixed, instinctive movement patterns, which, especially in lower animals, appear only under specific hormonal states and in response to sign stimuli (particular complicated configurations of stimulus elements). Such instinctive acts are often not subject to correction and control by an animal. Once elicited, they must be completed, even if they fail to produce their normal outcome.

When we speak of purposive behavior, we mean acts that are directed toward a goal and are accompanied by a corresponding motivation to reach that goal. The essential quality is the motivational state—the physiological central state that corresponds to the urge to perform a given act, to obtain a certain object, or to produce a desired outcome. If we could be sure that such a state exists during a given act, we could justifiably call that act motivated behavior.

Clearly, when an act is a completely automatic consequence of a stimulus, we need not speak of motivation. As long as a fixed built-in relation exists between a stimulus and a response, we have no justification for inferring the additional existence of a motivational state underlying that response to the stimulus. Such a state may exist, but we have no proof of it. Only when we can be sure that a central motivational state exists apart from the stimulus and the response, may we speak of motivated behavior.

To infer motivation, we must break the fixed connection between stimulus and response. The learning process enables us to do so. Let us consider one of the examples of apparently purposive behavior mentioned above—the rat who presses a bar to obtain food. How do we train an animal to perform such an operant act? (This is the name given to this type of learned behavior by B. F. Skinner, the psychologist who most thoroughly studied it). We arbitrarily choose almost any act from the animal's repertoire and reinforce the act (that is, increase the animal's tendency to perform it) with food, water, or whatever else the animal will work to obtain. Although typically psychologists teach a rat to press a bar or a pigeon to peck a key, we could as readily have trained either animal to dance around the cage if we so chose. In training, we ordinarily make the animal hungry and use food as a reinforcement, but we can use water for thirsty animals, or the termination or avoidance of painful electric shock to reward an animal for performing the appropriate act. We usually use a light to signal the delivery of a pellet, but we can use a tone or a buzzer or any other stimulus the animal can detect. The animal can also exert control over the occurrence of his response or whether he will respond at all. These characteristics of a learned act—the arbitrary, essentially interchangeable nature of the act and of the stimulus that elicits it, as well as the measure of control the animal exerts over the response—distinguish it as a voluntary act. Once learned, such a voluntary act can be used for any reinforcement. Thus, unlike many instinctive responses, the bar press response can be separated from the animal's internal state. In effect, in any operant situation, the stimulus, the response, and the reinforcement are completely arbitrary. No one of them bears any biologically built-in, fixed connection to the others. We arrange the experimental situation so that the response produces the reward and the animal *learns* the connection between them.

Once having learned this relationship, the animal reveals its motivation by working to obtain the reinforcement. This is what all operant-conditioning situations have in common: the animal's motivation to obtain reinforcement. By taking advantage of the animal's capacity to learn, and by training it to respond with an arbitrary voluntary act to obtain a given reinforcement, we can be sure the animal is motivated. If an operant occurs, motivation exists.

DRIVE VERSUS MOTIVE

Does motivation exist in animals low on the phylogenetic scale of evolutionary development? Consider an insect such as the common blowfly, often found buzzing around garbage dumps or animal stables. Is it hungry? Is it searching for food as it buzzes around a heap of garbage? Vincent G. Dethier, a zoologist-psychologist at the University of Pennsylvania, has developed methods for studying how the blowfly feeds. Flies eat and thrive on pure sugar solutions. The longer a blowfly has been without food, the lower the sugar-concentration it accepts, and the more of a given concentration it will eat. Thus, food-deprivation facilitates its approach to and ingestion of food. This looks like motivated behavior, but if we demand independent proof of motivation, as a central state existing independently of built-in nervous reflexes, we find that we are not yet able to say that the fly is hungry—that is, that it wants to obtain food. The act of eating in the blowfly is completely reflexive. It is a stereotyped chain of acts: When the fly happens to step into a droplet of a sweet substance, taste receptors on its legs are stimulated chemically, the fly reflexively extends its tonguelike proboscis, and it sucks the fluid. Whether or not the response occurs depends entirely on the state of sensory adaptation of the taste receptors and on signals transmitted from the foregut via a nerve (the recurrent nerve), that runs back to the fly's brain. When the sensory threshold is low, the response occurs unless inhibited by signals from the foregut. Eating is a fixed automatic response over which the fly apparently has no control. We conclude this because if the recurrent nerve is sectioned, inhibition no longer occurs, and feeding is continued automatically until the fly bursts from overeating. Although Dethier has tried many times, with many methods, he has not yet been able to prove that a fly can learn anything, much less use some arbitrary response to obtain food. Therefore, we cannot say that the fly wants to eat.

However, the reflexes involved in feeding are clearly easier to elicit when the fly has been deprived and are more difficult to elicit when its foregut is full. Its general level of activity is higher when deprived and therefore it is more likely to encounter food, and more easily stimulated when it does so. The internal state of the fly does influence the excitability of its nervous system, and does control its feeding reflexes. Such a state, which is characteristic of all instinctive activities, can be called a drive state. A hunger drive exists: The fly's approach to and acceptance of food are increased automatically, in contrast to motivated behavior, where a central state apart from reflexes can be inferred each time the animal uses an arbitrary act to obtain food. As Dethier has pointed out, perhaps by using insects such as the honey bee, which are clearly capable of learning, it may be possible to demonstrate and study various motivations in insects. Like rats, they may be trained to do arbitrary voluntary acts to obtain food. These acts can serve as an indication of the animal's hunger for food, independent of the fixed reflexes normally involved in eating.

We have been talking about relatively gross differences in levels of behavior: reflexes, instincts, and voluntary acts. They share elements in common, yet differ in their level of complexity. Still, there must be laws of nervous function within each level, and those laws common to all levels are probably general principles of nervous function. The differences between levels should provide a clue to understanding how complex behavior is built up from simpler building blocks. This sets the problem for a physiological understanding of behavior: What are the laws that govern each level of behavior? How are they similar and how are they different? And how does the nervous system act to produce them?

Developmental Synthesis
of Behavior

Reflexes are psychologically significant because of the way they are integrated into more complex behavioral acts. The spinal preparations discussed in the preceding pages show that simple automatisms (automatic movements) are coordinated into complex postures and sequential movement patterns. By cutting the spinal cord, we isolate fragments of behavior from the motivated, instinctive, or voluntary acts in which they are normally embedded. But the technique of spinal section, which we use to reveal these reflexes, destroys the possibility of observing other complex automatisms that can exist only if the connections with higher

60

6

parts of the nervous system remain intact. Is there any way of simplifying behavior without destroying the natural integrity of the nervous system?

The newborn infant possesses only the barest rudiments of behavior. It sleeps and wakes, nurses at its mother's breast, and, when in distress, cries and struggles. We cannot be sure how well it sees, since it does not appear to follow moving stimuli with its eyes, and is incapable of any voluntary directed action. Yet, a few months later, it smiles at its mother's face, watches her movements, reaches out to grasp a bottle of milk brought before its eyes, and brings the nipple to its mouth for feeding in a well-directed voluntary act. How does its behavior develop? Are there simple components which become integrated into more complex behavioral acts?

The newborn infant possesses many of the reflexes seen in spinal preparations. Reflexes can be understood in terms of their function. They increase or decrease the infant's contact with the stimuli evoking them. In general, we can distinguish two classes: (1) reflexes of approach which are elicited by stimuli of weak intensity and which serve to increase the opportunity for contact with the stimulus; and (2) reflexes of withdrawal which serve to terminate the noxious stimulus, and are usually evoked by intense stimuli.

Reflexes of Approach

Rooting. As shown in Figure 6-1, touching a rubber nipple to the cheek or chin of a newborn infant will immediately elicit the rooting reflex, a head movement that serves to bring the mouth closer to the nipple. At the same time, the mouth opens, and if it contacts the nipple, it closes over it and the infant begins to suck. These reflexes are completely automatic and can occur

Figure 6-1 Rooting reflex of a newborn infant on being touched with a nipple. (A and B) Turning of the head around its vertical axis, to the right and left side. (C and D) Turning of the head around its transverse axis, upward and downward. (A and D) Opening of the mouth to grasp the nipple. (A. Peiper. Cerebral Function in Infancy and Childhood. New York: Consultants Bureau, 1963, p. 405.)

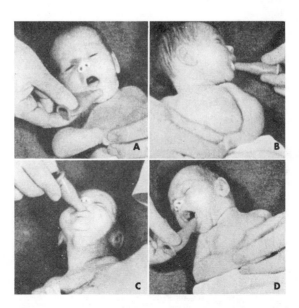

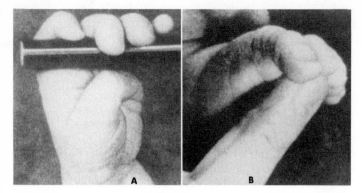

Figure 6-2 (A) Palmar grasp reflex of newborn. Touching the palm causes flexion of fingers and grasping of the touching object. (B) Plantar grasp reflex of newborn. Pressure on anterior of the sole causes flexion of toes. (A. Peiper. Cerebral Function in Infancy and Childhood. New York: Consultants Bureau, 1963, p. 159.)

when the infant is asleep or in a coma. They bring the infant into contact with the mother's breast and enable the infant to feed.

Grasping. Touching the infant's palm causes its fingers to flex and close around the stimulating object. This is the grasp reflex (Figure 6-2). There is also a grasp reflex of the foot. Pressure on the anterior end of the sole causes downward flexion of the toes. Both these grasp reflexes serve to increase and maintain the contact of hand and foot with the stimulating object. They are extremely powerful. If the infant is caused to grasp a rope reflexively with its hands as in Figure 6-3 A and B, it will cling so firmly that it can support itself entirely when suspended in midair. As shown in Figure 6-3 C, the posture adopted by a newborn infant when clinging to a rope with hands and feet bears a curiously close resemblance to that adopted by a tree-sloth hanging upside down from the branch of a tree.

Reflexes of Withdrawal

As seen in Figure 6-4A, if a bright light is flashed into an infant's eyes it will shut them instantly, thus

Figure 6-3 Grasp reflex in a prematurely born 4-week-old twin (weight 2300 gm). (A) Arm suspension from the palmar grasp reflex. (B) Arm suspension with simultaneous leg suspension from palmar and plantar grasp reflexes. (C) Sloth suspended from a tree. (A. Peiper. Cerebral Function in Infancy and Childhood. *New York: Consultants Bureau, 1963, p. 162.)*

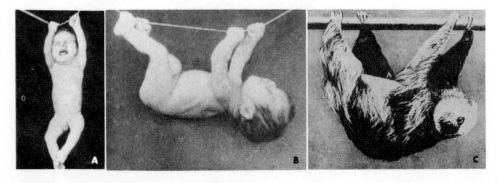

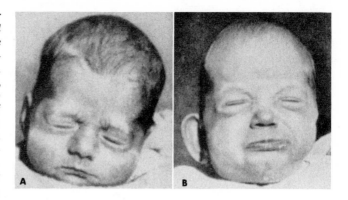

Figure 6-4 **(A)** *Behavior of a 7½-week-old girl (1200 gm) on exposure to a blinding light stimulus. Note closed mouth.* **(B)** *Facial reaction, spreading from mouth to eyes, caused by intake of 3% quinine in a girl 2½ months old. (A. Peiper.* Cerebral Function in Infancy and Childhood. *New York: Consultants Bureau, 1963, pp. 45, 112.)*

cutting off the blinding visual stimulus. Similarly (Figure 6-4B), a bitter taste causes immediate rejection and firm closure of the mouth, with down-turned corners. Painful stimulation of the hand elicits a withdrawal reflex, characterized by spreading extension of the fingers, and, if the stimulus is sufficiently strong, flexion of hand and arm, which serves to pull them away from the stimulus. A similar reflex is seen in the foot. Painful stimulation of the sole of the foot elicits the Babinski reflex: a spreading of the toes. If the stimulus is intense enough the entire leg is withdrawn.

Spread of Reflexes

How do these simple re-flexes become integrated into more complex forms of behavior? We have seen in the preceding figures one principle of elaboration of reflexes into more complex acts. Reflexes spread in response to increased intensity of stimulation. Allied reflexes, those which have in common the function of approach or withdrawal, occur together to cooperate in approach or avoidance of the stimulus. For instance, the rooting reflex can occur alone. If, however, the infant has been long without food, or if its cheek is stroked repeatedly with the nipple, then vigorous headturning will occur in combination with mouth-opening and sucking. Similarly, bright light elicits eye-closure; bitter quinine, mouth-closure; intense stimuli of either type can elicit both, combined with a turning away of the head. The foot-withdrawal reflex can consist merely in

Figure 6-5 **(A)** *Stepping movements of a newborn.* **(B)** *Ascending movements of a newborn. (A. Peiper.* Cerebral Function in Infancy and Childhood. *New York: Consultants Bureau, 1963, pp. 212 and 213.)*

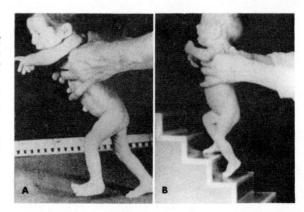

a fanning of the toes. However, if the stimulus is intense enough, these actions occur in combination with upward flexion of the ankle, knee, and thigh. The foot withdrawal has become a mass reflex—a withdrawal of the entire leg. Thus, simple reflexes can combine into chains in response to strong stimuli. These chains make the response more effective in approach to, or withdrawal from, stimuli. The nervous mechanism responsible for such a spread of allied reflexes must be basic to the integration of chains of behavior.

Reflex Chains

A newborn infant cannot stand upright, but if its body is supported so that its legs are placed in contact with the surface of the floor below, and its body is moved forward, then smoothly synchronized stepping movements occur (Figure 6-5A). Similarly, if the child is moved forward while being held upright so that its legs come into contact with the surfaces of a staircase (Figure 6-5B), stepping movements appear which are involved in the normal coordinated act of walking upstairs. The infant cannot walk voluntarily; therefore, the presence at birth of such reflex chains shows that they are inborn nervous patterns which await the development of voluntary control mechanisms.

LEVEL OF FUNCTION IN THE NEWBORN INFANT

The Anencephalic versus the Normal Newborn Infant

Some infants who have developed abnormally *in utero,* are born with incompletely formed nervous systems. These infants, called anencephalic, usually die very quickly, but in rare instances they live for days or months, long enough for a relatively complete assessment of their behavioral capacities. Such infants characteristically have incompletely developed heads, with bulbous, frog-like eyes, and relatively long prehensile fingers. One such infant died after several days, and at autopsy it was found to be devoid of any nervous tissue above the medulla, although its spinal cord and medulla appeared to be normally developed. Yet the behavior of anencephalic children at birth is amazingly similar in many respects to that of a normal newborn child. They root, suck, and nurse at the mother's breast. They grasp with hand and foot. In response to a pin prick, the foot withdraws normally, perhaps even exaggeratedly—slight stimuli easily produce mass reflex withdrawal of the entire leg. These infants, however, do not cry or move spontaneously.

Another anencephalic infant was found to have a somewhat more completely developed nervous system. Although lacking cerebral hemispheres and cerebellum, it possessed a relatively normal spinal cord, medulla, and midbrain. It, too, displayed normal rooting, sucking, grasp, and withdrawal reflexes. In contrast to the anencephalic infant lacking a midbrain, it breathed without any difficulty, and showed clear patterns of waking and sleeping similar to those of a normal newborn. It nursed, but not sufficiently to gain or even to maintain its weight. It steadily lost weight and would have died within a few days if it had not been tube-fed. However, with the help of tube-feeding, it lived for 57 days. Like the other anencephalic child, it did not cry or show any spontaneous movement. Like Flourens' decerebrate pigeon, these anencephalic children are reflex machines.

As we have seen, the normal child at birth is in many ways comparable to an animal without cerebral hemispheres, that is, incapable of voluntary action. Yet it differs from the anencephalic infant; it is a squirming bundle of spontaneous activity, screaming and struggling when wet, cold, hungry, or in pain. Feed it, bundle it in warm dry wrappings, and it subsides into peaceful relaxation, gurgling in contentment, and soon lapses into sleep. Like the hypothalamic cat, its behavior is more instinctive than reflexive; the thresholds of its reflexes and its spontaneous activities are strongly influenced, not merely by external stimuli, but by its internal state as well. Is the spontaneous cyclical activity of the normal newborn due to the presence of an intact hypothalamus? Would an anencephalic infant, possessed of a normal hypothalamus also show vigorous spontaneous activity, strong emotions of pleasure and discomfort, normal patterns of sleep, and well-regulated feeding behavior? We do not yet know. This is an important question that future experiments on animals should be able to answer.

THE DEVELOPMENT OF COMPLEX BEHAVIOR

By the age of eight months or so, the normal infant has developed a much more complex pattern of behavior than it possessed at birth. It orients and pays attention to moving objects and sounds in the room. It smiles at its mother's face, and laughs with pleasure at a funny face or sound, or when swung in the air. The sight of its bottle evokes instant attention in the hungry infant, with orientation of the head, visual following, and well-directed voluntary reaching for the bottle (see Figure 6-6). When the bottle is presented, the child grasps it eagerly and sucks the nipple vigorously. At this age he crawls around the floor, reaches for bright, interesting objects, and will, within a few more months, be able to walk and begin to talk.

These acts are not automatic reflexes, though many of their components resemble the innate reflexes present at birth. How do we know this? After all, the infant at birth is in many ways comparable to a decerebrate animal. Don't we have the problem of anthropomorphism equally when dealing with infants as when trying to understand the behavior of lower animals? Can't we be just as mistaken in attributing our own adult feelings and desires, our own thoughts and intentions, to an infant, a cat, a rat, a chicken, or an insect? Perhaps. But the child does eventually become a man with his own thoughts, emotions, and desires. Isn't it oversimplifying, then, to try to explain his behavior in terms of simple automatisms such as reflexes? How do we distinguish the appropriate level of behavioral complexity he has achieved at any stage of his development?

The whole basis of a physiological approach to the study of behavior rests on the assumption that there are various kinds of simple building blocks of behavior which combine in a complicated form to produce the behavioral phenomena we are trying to understand. We have seen that by cutting through the nervous system at different levels, or by studying the behavior of newborn

Developmental
Synthesis
of Behavior

infants, we discover several levels of behavior: reflexes, instincts, and motivated voluntary behavior. At each level, we are beginning to work out the laws governing such behavior. But to profit from such knowledge we must be able to recognize what level of behavior is being manifested. We must be able to distinguish a reflex from an instinctive or a voluntary act, an automatism from a purposeful act, a learned response from an innate one, a conscious from an unconscious act, and so forth. We must, therefore, formulate diagnostic behavioral signs that tell us what type of behavior we are dealing with.

Consider the child in Figure 6-7. She is nearly a year old, now capable of many voluntary acts. If held in an oblique position, she immediately adopts a characteristic bowed posture of leg, arm, and head. The upper limbs are flexed, and it seems as though she is trying to maintain her equilibrium in air by keeping her head erect and adjusting her limbs to maintain her balance. But is this postural adjustment voluntary? No. It is a reflex postural chain completely elicited and maintained by the position of the head. If the child's head is gently bent forward, her limbs collapse and she hangs limply in the air.

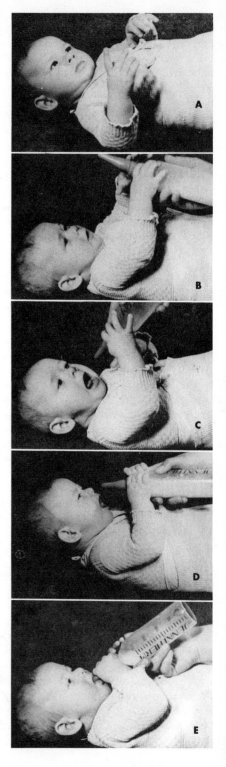

Figure 6-6   Conditioned reactions of a five-month-old bottle-fed infant on seeing the bottle, before it touches his mouth. (A) Infant at rest. (B) He looks at the approaching bottle, his hands reach out, and his mouth is opened. (C) Wide opening of the mouth, protrusion of the tongue, efforts to bring the bottle to his mouth with his hands. (D) The same, the head is raised with mouth wide open and approaches the bottle. (E) Starting of food intake. (A. Peiper. Cerebral Function in Infancy and Childhood. New York: Consultants Bureau, 1963, p. 450.)

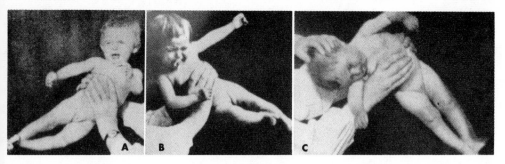

Figure 6-7 Asymmetrical chain reflex with the body in suspended oblique lateral position and head up. (A) Left lateral position. (B) Right lateral position. (C) Extinction of suspension reflex in right lateral position by passive lowering of head. (A. Peiper. Cerebral Function in Infancy and Childhood. *New York: Consultants Bureau, 1963, p. 188.)*

The complete dependence of her body posture on the position of her head shows that the child is not striving to maintain equilibrium, but is automatically making a reflex adjustment of her body in relation to the position of her head. We see, then, how important it is to identify the degree of complexity being exhibited in behavior.

The Disappearance of Reflexes as Behavior Develops

The simple involuntary reflexes present in the infant at birth disappear as development progresses. By the age of four to six months, the automatic grasp reflex of hand and foot, the rooting and sucking reflexes of the mouth, the coordinated stepping patterns seen earlier, all become increasingly difficult to elicit as the capacity for voluntary reaching, grasping, eating, and walking develop. Eventually, voluntary purposeful acts dominate the behavior of the child; reflexes seem to disappear.

Does this mean they are no longer a part of his behavior? Can we neglect these simpler units in an attempt to understand his behavior? Has he used these simple mechanisms merely as crutches during his early development only to cast them away when he becomes capable of the amazingly complex behavior of the adult human being?

Clearly, they are still present in the nervous system. Men have had their spinal cord completely severed by accident. The lower half of the body is then completely cut off from the brain—no sensations are felt in the body below the level of the section and no voluntary movements can be made with the limbs controlled by the nervous system below the section. Yet, in these limbs the grasp and withdrawal reflexes seen in infancy can be elicited. Therefore, the reflex mechanisms are present, even though they remain in the background when the nervous system is intact.

As the nervous system develops, the simple reflex movement patterns are transformed into more complex behavioral acts. They become subject to voluntary control. We must learn to recognize their existence and discover how they operate now that they are subject to more complicated forms of nervous control. We must unravel the means by which the higher parts of the nervous system integrate these simple patterns into complex acts.

Sleep
and Wakefulness

The automatisms of approach and avoidance displayed by the newborn infant are seen usually while it is awake, about eight hours out of every 24. For two-thirds of the time, the newborn child sleeps and its reflexes are greatly inhibited, in contrast to the reflexes seen in a spinal cat, where no cyclic depression of spinal excitability occurs. Indeed, even the anencephalic infant, with only the medulla and midbrain added to its spinal cord, shows periodic quiescence in which its reflexes are difficult to elicit. However, if these higher structures are not developed, the anencephalic infant, like the spinal cat, shows no sleep. A "sleep center"

68

7

must exist in the hind brain which produces periods of bodily sleep by rhythmically inhibiting the spinal motor cells involved in approach and avoidance, making them inaccessible to the external stimuli clamoring for reflex responses. Clearly, a systematic timeout for rest, recovery, rebuilding, and growth is a way of protecting the infant from exhaustion and of refreshing it for the new energy requirements involved in its next waking episode. For it must wake up to eat.

But, as the brain develops, the child becomes capable of voluntary, directed activities. The infantile behavior of falling asleep automatically after a period of waking will then become a hindrance rather than a help. In a sense, the sleep of the body is no longer suited to the needs of the developing brain. Voluntary control over sleep must replace reflexive automatic sleep. As voluntary behavior develops, the brain must stay awake for longer and longer periods. Indeed, if the sleep-and-wakefulness cycle of the infant is measured, as in Figure 7-1, this process is clearly revealed: During the first six weeks after birth, the infant sleeps about the same amount (16 out of each 24 hours), but more and more of the sleep he needs is obtained at night. Gradually, the sleep requirement is lessened, enabling the brain to stay awake for longer and longer periods during the day, till by the age of 14–18 years a fourfold increase in wakefulness has been achieved: A waking-sleep ratio of 1:2 in the infant gives way to the 2:1 ratio of the adult. Eight hours sleep a night is now sufficient, leaving the brain awake the rest of the time. A wakefulness of choice has been superimposed on the wakefulness of necessity.

THE WAKING BRAIN

How does the brain stay awake? Our knowledge of the neurophysiology of wakefulness stems from two basic facts, discovered within a few years of each other. In 1929, Hans Berger discovered that the electrical activity of the human brain can be detected by a galvanometer through metal-plate electrodes placed on the skin of the scalp. Furthermore, the electroencephalogram, or EEG (the written record of these brain potentials), of the waking subject is

Figure 7-1   A schematic representation of the change with development from the primitive polycyclic alternation of sleep and wakefulness in the newborn infant to the monocyclic sleep-wakefulness rhythm in the adult. The 50- to 60-minute basic rest-activity periodicity in the infant, shown in the small waves, is gradually lengthened to 80–90 minutes in the adult. Black areas represent sleep. (N. Kleitman. Sleep and Wakefulness. Chicago: Univ. of Chicago Press, 1963, p. 367.)

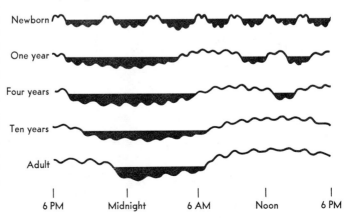

quite different from that of the sleeping person. The brain when awake shows the unsynchronized, low-voltage, fast activity depicted in Figure 7-2 (voltages fluctuating rapidly around 20 to 25 cycles per second). This unsynchronized pattern indicates that the cells of the cerebral cortex are firing in patterns which are largely independent of each other. Since they are mostly out of phase, they tend to average out and large potentials do not appear.

As we fall asleep, so-called "spindle" bursts of larger amplitude waves appear (Figure 7-2), indicating that groups of cortical cells are beginning to fire in unison. As neighboring cells become synchronized, their summed voltage grows and then decays as they simultaneously grow refractory, thus giving the spindle shape to the burst. More frequent spindles occur, and more and more cells are recruited, so that eventually synchronized waves of activity

Figure 7-2   Normal EEG records characteristic of different stages on the sleep-wakefulness continuum. The only major omission in the series would be between excited *and* relaxed, *where there should be a low-voltage record resembling* excited, *but with less marked activation, labelled* attentive. *(D. B. Lindsley. "Attention, Consciousness, Sleep, and Wakefulness." In J. Field (ed.),* Handbook of Physiology, Section I, Neurophysiology, Vol. III, *pp. 1553–1593. After H. H. Jasper.* Epilepsy and Cerebral Localization, *edited by W. Penfield and T. C. Erickson. Springfield: Thomas, 1941, p. 401.)*

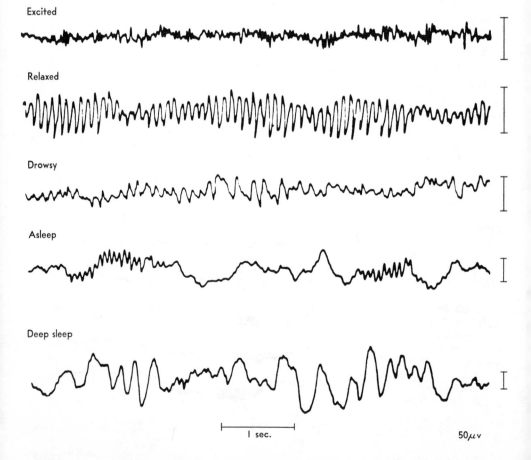

Excited

Relaxed

Drowsy

Asleep

Deep sleep

1 sec.

50µv

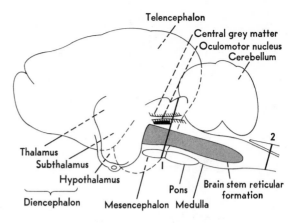

Figure 7-3 Drawing of the cat brain. Transection through the midbrain (line labelled 1) yields the cerveau isolé *preparation with constant slow-wave sleep EEG patterns in the brain above. Transection through the spinal cord (line labelled 2) yields the* encephale isolé *preparation with normal waking-sleep patterns in the brain above. (Adapted from G. Moruzzi. Endeavour, 1963, 22, 31–36.)*

sweep across the cortex like waves on the beach. This is the EEG picture of the sleeping brain—synchronized, high-amplitude (up to 100 microvolts or more), slow (2 to 3 per second) waves, mixed with spindle bursts.

A few years later in 1935, the Belgian neurophysiologist Frédéric Brémer investigated the electrical activity of the brain of the cat. He found that the EEG of cat and man are much alike: desynchronized, low-voltage, fast activity while awake and synchronized, high-voltage, slow waves when asleep. Even if the cat's spinal cord is separated from the rest of the encephalon (brain) by a cervical section (cutting through the spinal cord in the neck), the isolated cephalic structures above (*encephale isolé*) still show normal sleeping and waking EEG patterns that correspond with behavioral patterns of sleeping and waking. But if the cerebral hemispheres are separated from the lower nervous structures by a section through the midbrain (*cerveau isolé*), the brain above the section shows continuous synchronization—it is permanently asleep.

The *cerveau isolé* preparation cuts off all sensory input to the brain except for visual and olfactory stimuli. Brémer therefore concluded that the sensory input normally bombarding the intact nervous system keeps the brain awake. When we diminish these stimuli—that is, when we turn out the lights, close our eyes, lie down on a soft bed, and relax—the brain falls passively asleep.

THE ASCENDING RETICULAR ACTIVATING SYSTEM

Strong stimuli wake us from sleep. How do they reach the brain? An American physiologist, Horace W. Magoun, his Italian co-worker, Giuseppe Moruzzi, and a psychologist, Donald B. Lindsley, answered this question with an analysis of the *cerveau isolé* preparation. A complete section of the midbrain produces a sleeping brain above the level of the section. By making partial sections, one should be able to isolate the relevant ascending systems which conduct to the brain stimuli to keep it awake. Consider the cross-section of the midbrain (Figure 7-4). The ascending pathways can be divided into two groups: The long sensory pathways from the muscles and skin of the body lie in the lateral portions of the midbrain. These long sensory pathways go primarily to nuclei in the dorsal thalamus, which in turn project

Sleep
and
Wakefulness

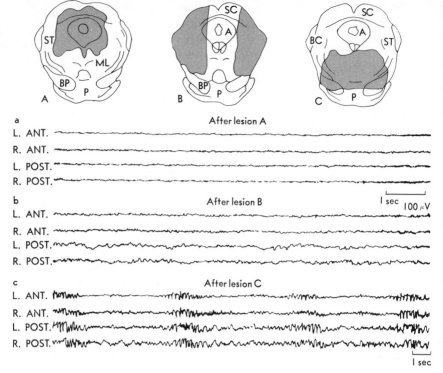

Figure 7-4   The EEG pattern of sleep of the cerveau isolé *preparation may be obtained with lesions of the floor of the mesencephalon (C). Destruction of the central grey matter (A) or of the lateral areas containing the main sensory pathways (B) do not have such an effect. Records a, b, and c represent cortical EEG patterns after lesions A, B, or C. Tinted areas represent lesions. (Adapted from D. B. Lindsley, J. W. Bowden, and H. W. Magoun. EEG and Clin. Neurophysiol., 1949, 1, 475–486.)*

on separate areas of the cortex. Thus, the dorsal thalamus is related to the lateral surfaces of the cortex. These are the specific sensory systems which project to specific sensory areas and they are involved in conscious, precisely discriminated sensation. One might consider them to be the stream of thought.

In the middle of the midbrain, around the central canal, is another ascending system—the reticular formation (Figure 7-5), a collection of cells with short fibers having many branches which connect diffusely like a meshwork; i.e., like a reticulum. This reticular system receives short collateral side branches from the long ascending specific fiber tracts and connects to the structures of the diencephalon which lie close to the middle of the brain— the midline and ventral thalamic nuclei and, below them, the hypothalamus. Unlike the dorsal thalamic cells, which project to specific areas of the cortex, the reticular thalamic cells project diffusely to many areas of the cortex. The hypothalamus is related to the older parts of the forebrain which develop early in evolution—the primitive "smell brain," also called the rhinencephalon, made up of structures lying in the middle walls of the brain. Also in contrast to the specific system in the dorsal thalamus, the cells of the midline thalamus

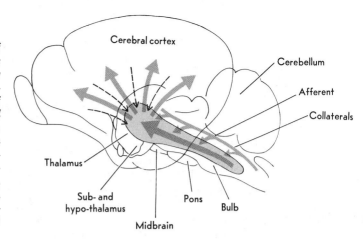

Figure 7-5 Outline of brain of cat showing the extent of the medially placed ascending reticular-activating system of the brain stem (shaded area) and the distribution of collaterals to it from the laterally situated ascending sensory pathways. (T. E. Starzl, C. W. Taylor, and H. W. Magoun. J. Neurophysiol., 1951, 14, 479–496.)

Labels in figure: Cerebral cortex; Cerebellum; Afferent; Collaterals; Thalamus; Sub- and hypo-thalamus; Midbrain; Pons; Bulb

and hypothalamus receive an unspecific diffuse sensory input from many sense modalities. The sensations they give rise to must be vague, poorly differentiated, and difficult to identify. One might think of them as the stream of feelings and emotions.

As shown in Figure 7-4, Moruzzi, Magoun, and Lindsley destroyed the lateral areas in the brain stem, thereby cutting off the specific sensory pathways to the brain. The cat's sleep was unimpaired—the normal cycles of waking and sleeping appeared in the EEG, and normal sleep and waking behavior were present. But if only the reticular system was destroyed, leaving the lateral specific pathways intact, the cat slept all the time. It could be aroused by strong stimuli. It woke up and the EEG showed desynchronization, but within a few moments, its EEG became synchronized again, and the cat fell back to sleep. Conversely, electrical stimulation of the reticular formation by implanted electrodes in a normal sleeping cat woke it up and it remained awake. Clearly, the local desynchronization produced by specific impulses to specific cortical projection areas was not sufficient to keep the brain awake. The diffuse reticular system (see Figure 7-5) with input from many sensory systems and projections all over the cortex was necessary for activation of the sleeping brain and for maintained wakefulness.

THE SLEEPING BRAIN

Does the brain sleep passively, that is, only in the absence of the sensory stimuli which act through the reticular system to keep it awake? This was the simplest explanation, and one which was generally believed even after Walter Rudolph Hess, a Swiss neurophysiologist, in 1931 published his work on electrical stimulation of the brain. Hess was interested in studying the effects of stimulation of structures lying deep in the brain. Because he wanted to study complex instinctive behavior, which could only be observed in conscious waking animals, he developed a system of implanting insulated wires deep in the brain of the cat. An external socket fixed to the cat's skull allows it to live normally yet to be hooked up for electrical brain stimulation during its normal waking activities. Hess found that stimulation of the midline structures of the thalamus with electrical impulses of low frequency (5 to 6 cycles per second) induced a normal waking cat to show all the signs of normal sleep. The cat searched for a comfortable place, curled up, settled down, and went to sleep for long periods of time. This result was in contrast to that of stimulation in certain other parts of the brain, which had the opposite effect—it roused the animal to vigorous activity, often fight or flight. Hess thought that there are two antagonistic systems in the brain. He called one the ergotrophic system, that which integrates the actions of those bodily systems, both skeletal and vegetative, that the animal uses in vigorous action. The other system, the trophotropic system, is involved in those activities, such as sleep, rest, and digestion, which serve to conserve energy and replenish reserves.

Because electrical stimulation of the brain actively induces sleep and all the preparatory behavior leading up to it, sleep is not merely the passive absence of wakefulness. This assertion is reminiscent of an early finding of Ivan Pavlov, that dogs being conditioned to salivate to stimuli signaling the presentation of food, regularly fell asleep in the apparatus when learning to inhibit their response to other stimuli, which Pavlov chose not to reinforce. Conditioned inhibition produces sleep. Pavlov reasoned that a local inhibitory process is set up in the brain which spreads throughout the cortex and produces sleep. This is not unlike the notion that a synchronous inhibitory process recruits cortical cells into the slow simultaneous rhythmic activity that corresponds to the EEG rhythm seen in sleep. It should be noted that the frequency of stimulation that Hess found effective (5 to 6 cycles per second) is very close to that of a synchronized EEG. Indeed, it has been found in recent years that stimulation in many areas of the brain, cortex, thalamus, midbrain, and even in the reticular system, will induce sleep if it is of low intensity and is repeated for long periods at the frequency of the EEG. Thus, external stimuli as well as stimulation in many parts of the brain can actively produce sleep by recruiting cortical cells into synchronous activity.

Recent evidence has been found which confirms the existence of localized brain structures that actively induce sleep. High-frequency electrical stimulation (which is typically arousing in many parts of the brain) will induce sleep if the electrodes are located in the front part of the hypothalamus—the preoptic area. This discovery agrees with earlier findings by Walle H. Nauta that damage to this area produces sleeplessness in rats. They do not sleep at all and die within a few days. Lesions in the posterior hypothalamus, near the reticular activating system, produce somnolence. If preoptic lesions are combined with posterior ones, sleeplessness does not cancel out somnolence —the animals remain somnolent. This finding suggests that the preoptic sleep system acts by inhibiting the reticular activating system of which the posterior hypothalamus is a part. Rául Hernández-Peón and his co-workers in Mexico have recently discovered that they can chemically activate this sleep system in the cat's preoptic area by implanting crystals of acetylcholine through hollow tubes. By this method they have shown that a whole system of sleep-producing structures descends from the preoptic area, through the lateral hypothalamus to the midbrain. It is likely that these structures function by inhibiting the reticular activating system.

What has happened to the primitive sleep of the body seen in the infant? Has the developing brain so completely taken over that, like the reflexes of infancy, primitive sleep completely disappears? This problem was largely ignored until 1958, when the psychologist William Dement discovered that in the sleep of adult man and cat, there is a stage of very deep sleep during which the EEG is desynchronized (low-amplitude, fast activity). This has been called "paradoxical sleep" because the EEG resembles that of a waking brain, but the subject is so deeply asleep that only the strongest external stimuli can wake him. Indeed, so profound is this sleep, that spontaneous muscular activity as recorded by the electromyograph (EMG) disappears almost completely, with a consequent drop in blood pressure. But there is some activity: The eyes continuously move rapidly back and forth and breathing becomes uneven with sporadic deep inspirations. Also, paradoxical sleep seems to be that period of sleep when dreams occur. If people are awakened during, or just after such a stage, they nearly always report that they were dreaming and can describe their dreams vividly. In contrast, if awakened during slow-wave sleep they rarely recall dreaming. Furthermore, people need this dream stage of sleep; if they are repeatedly prevented from dreaming for several days by being awakened whenever they enter the rapid-eye movement (REM) dream state (but are allowed as much slow-wave sleep as they wish), they become progressively more and more irritable. When subsequently allowed undisturbed sleep, they show a marked increase in the amount of time spent dreaming, as though they were making up a deficit.

The neurophysiological basis of paradoxical sleep has been carefully analyzed since 1959 by the French physiologist Michel Jouvet. Like Brémer, Magoun, and Moruzzi, he studied the brain of the cat, with various kinds of sections and removals. But he studied the sleep of the body as well as that of the brain. What he found will enable us to understand paradoxical sleep and its relation to slow-wave sleep.

Jouvet observed, in corroboration of previous work, that the *cerveau isolé* cat brain shows continuous sleep—a permanently synchronized EEG. But if he measured the electrical activity of the brain below the section, and also the muscular activity of the cat's body, he found that there are still cyclic periods of waking and sleeping in the nervous system below the midbrain section. The body of the *cerveau isolé* cat shows regular periods of muscular quiescence corresponding to those existing during paradoxical sleep in cat and man. This means that the rhythmic sleep of the body can occur independently of the higher brain structures, just as we saw earlier in the anencephalic child whose brain has not developed.

Furthermore, paradoxical sleep persists in the brain of the cat even after complete destruction of the reticular formation. The EEG of the brain is for the most part synchronized, as Magoun, Moruzzi, and Lindsley had found, but whenever bodily sleep occurs—that is, when muscular (EMG) activity disappears—the cortical EEG becomes desynchronized, just as it does during the normal paradoxical stage of sleep. Therefore, there must be two separate sleep systems—one for the brain and one for the body. The sleep center involved in bodily sleep is below the midbrain; via an ascending system apart from the reticular activating system, it desynchronizes the brain during paradoxical sleep. Jouvet set about locating this system. His results are summarized in Figures 7-6 and 7-7.

In the normal intact brain (Figure 7-6A), both sleep systems interact, producing the normal picture of three stages of sleep: (1) desynchronized EEG and high, spontaneous muscle activity (both brain and body awake), (2) synchronized slow-wave EEG with moderate muscular activity (brain asleep, body resting but not asleep), and (3) desynchronized EEG with no bodily muscle activity except rapid eye movements (brain awake and dreaming, but body asleep). In a decorticate cat (Figure 7-6B), no slow waves are seen in the remaining subcortical systems, but rhythmic bodily sleep is still present. Therefore, the cortex must be intact for the sleep of the brain (slow-wave sleep) to occur. Furthermore, the decorticate animal sleeps 90 per cent of the time (more than the normal 60 per cent) and all of it is paradoxical sleep; therefore, the cortex must exert an inhibitory influence which suppresses bodily sleep. This inhibition is probably one of the ways the cortex keeps itself awake. As described earlier, the brain of the midbrain cat (*cerveau isolé* with all ascending systems cut; Figure 7-6C) is permanently asleep, but below the section, rhythmic bodily wakefulness and sleep go on independent of the brain above. Lesions below the midbrain, in the caudal reticular nucleus in the pons, however (Figure 7-6D),

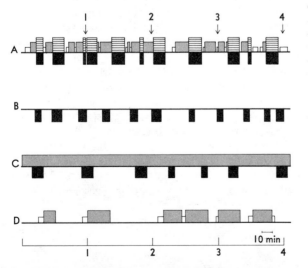

Figure 7-6 Diagrammatic representation of the sleep-wakefulness rhythm in (A) intact, (B) decorticate, (C) mesencephalic cats, and (D) cats with coagulation in the caudal reticular nucleus in the pons. Four hours of continuous recordings were taken in each cat. In black: paradoxical sleep with fast cortical EEG pattern in normal cats (horizontal hatching) and spindling activity at the pontine level, total disappearance of EMG activtiy, eye movements, in normal, decorticate, and mesencephalic cats. In white: spindling activity on the cortex. In gray: slow waves and spindles at the cortical and diencephalic level. Horizontal line: arousal. Note the absence of slow-wave sleep in decorticate cats, and the absence of paradoxical sleep in the cat with pontine lesions. (Adapted from M. Jouvet. Ciba Found. Symp. on The Nature of Sleep. London: J. & A. Churchill, Ltd., 1961, 188–208.)

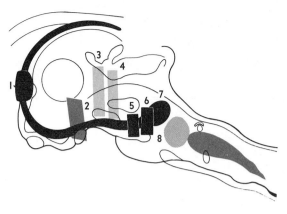

Figure 7-7 Schematic representation of the neural structures responsible for paradoxical sleep. In medium gray (8): Caudal reticular meleus in the pons whose destruction suppresses paradoxical sleep. In black: ascending limbic midbrain pathway anatomically mapped by other methods. (1–2–5–6) Lesions that suppress, totally or in part, the fast cortical activity induced during paradoxical sleep. In light gray (3–4): Lesions interrupting the ascending reticular activating system, at the mesencephalic level. These lesions which suppress cortical arousal do not eliminate the fast cortical activity induced during paradoxical sleep. In dark gray: Ponto-bulbar inhibitory reticular formation which is probably responsible for the inhibition of muscle activity during paradoxical sleep. (After M. Jouvet. Arch. Ital. Biol., 1962, 100, 125–206.)

completely obliterate bodily sleep. Periodic muscular relaxation does not occur, and paradoxical desynchronization of the EEG during slow-wave sleep is abolished. The brain sleeps dreamlessly, but the body remains awake.

Why does the brain wake up during bodily sleep? From the sleep center, in the pons, there must be a system that travels up to the brain in pathways separate from the midbrain reticular formation. By means of localized subcortical lesions, all of which eliminate the paradoxical desynchronization of the EEG which accompanies bodily sleep, Jouvet has isolated this system (see Figure 7-7): It travels from the floor of the midbrain through the lateral hypothalamus upward to the septal subcortical region, which is near the preoptic "sleep" center studied by Nauta and Hernández-Peón. It is interesting that paradoxical sleep occurs only after the brain has fallen asleep. We never dream until we have been in slow-wave sleep for a while. This suggests that bodily sleep is purely inhibitory—the pontile sleep center inhibits the nervous system above and below it: It inhibits the spinal reflexes, producing loss of EMG, and inhibits the cortical (preoptic?) sleep system active during slow-wave sleep. This wakes the brain, leaving it free to dream while the body is still deeply asleep.

Feeding

Starve a man, and food will dominate his life. When he is awake, he will desire food, think about it, hunt for it, kill for it. When he is asleep, food fills his dreams. How does food gain control of all his thoughts and actions? Consider him in more fortunate circumstances, where he can eat as often and as much as he likes. He eats more in cold weather, less in the heat, more when he works hard, less when inactive. He eats foods of wide variety, some packed with calories, others less nutritious, yet he can go along for years without much change in his body weight. He very beautifully adjusts his energy intake to his energy expenditure. How does he control his intake?

78

8

Once again, when faced with a complicated phenomenon, we begin by simplifying. The normal newborn infant wakes and eats. Like the anencephalic child, he eats reflexively. He shows rooting in response to contact with his mother's breast, grasps the nipple with his mouth, then sucks and swallows the milk that flows into it. The normal child eats enough to gain weight and grow. The anencephalic infant, however, without a brain above the midbrain, fails to eat enough and will soon die unless maintained by tube feeding.

The same is true of the adult decerebrate animal. James Woods, in the tradition of Philip Bard at The Johns Hopkins University Medical School, has prepared and successfully kept alive a number of decerebrate rats. In such a preparation, all of the brain is first removed above the hypothalamus. A section is then made behind the hypothalamus, cutting it off from the lower parts of the nervous system (midbrain, medulla, and spinal cord) leaving above only an isolated island of hypothalamic tissue connected to the pituitary gland to maintain hormonal control of general metabolic and growth functions. Such a rat can neither see nor smell. Its cage must be thermostatically controlled to keep its temperature within normal limits or it soon dies. However, in such a cage, it can live for months, displaying a remarkable range of behavior. It walks and grooms itself. When it comes into contact with a pellet of food, the rat grasps it, picks it up in its paws, and gnaws at it, chewing and swallowing the crumbs in its mouth. But, like an anencephalic child, it does not regulate its food intake. It must be tube-fed to be kept alive. Whether it is starved or full of food makes no difference. In either state, the reflexes of chewing, licking, and swallowing can be equally readily elicited. Without a forebrain, it knows neither hunger nor satiety.

It would be marvelous if someone would study a rat prepared in exactly the same way as the decerebrate, but with the hypothalamus left connected to the midbrain. If such a rat showed hunger and satiety, and could regulate its food intake, we would know, beyond any doubt, that structures in the hypothalamus add an essential dimension of control to the feeding reflexes. Just the way hormonal control is added to spinal sexual reflexes by hypothalamic structures (see pp. 55–56), so too could the internal environment exert hypothalamic control of feeding reflexes.

Regulation in the Infant

No one knows how the newborn infant regulates its food intake. It eats enough to gain weight. In contrast to the decerebrate rat, its food-approach reflexes (rooting, sucking, and swallowing) become more difficult to elicit after each meal, and are more easily evoked when the child has not eaten for some time. Stomach distension probably inhibits reflexive feeding in the infant, as has been clearly demonstrated in newborn puppies by putting milk into their stomach through a tube just before allowing them to nurse. With a full stomach, they suck much less. But do infants possess at birth all the regulatory capacities they will display when older? Do they adjust to caloric dilution, eat more in the cold or when they have been very active? Can a lowered amount of blood sugar increase their intake as it does in the adult? We do not yet know the answers to these questions.

As the child develops, the reflexes involved in feeding disappear along with the other automatisms of approach and avoidance (see pp. 60–67). Voluntary seeking, approach, and ingestion of food replace automatic feeding. In this transformation from reflexive to voluntary behavior, are new dimensions added to the control of food intake? How does the adult nervous system control feeding?

HYPOTHALAMIC CONTROL OF FEEDING

Adult food intake is multiply determined. Nature has provided several control systems, each of which acts to maintain the constancy of the internal environment (also called homeostasis). This is why scientific attempts to study feeding have so often been foiled. Removal of a single sensory signal (by removing the sense of taste, or smell, or even the entire stomach), for example, even though each one may be important in feeding, does not change total daily food intake. Apparently, homeostatic controls are designed to maintain a constant intake even if one or more of the normal signals are removed. To study such a system, we must damage the centers in the nervous system where the controls are integrated. By studying the aberrations that result, we can attempt to infer the nature of the normal controls.

For many years physicians at medical clinics have seen people who suffer from a growing tumor of the pituitary gland. The Viennese physician Alfred Fröhlich described their typical symptoms: tremendous obesity, and atrophy of the genital organs with decreased or absent sexual urge. Is the obesity seen in this syndrome due to disturbance of the pituitary gland or does it result from the pressure and damage that the tumor produces immediately above the pituitary gland in the hypothalamus? In 1927, animal experiments solved the problem. Careful removal of the pituitary gland in the rat, without damage to the brain above, does not result in obesity. However, if the hypothalamus is subsequently damaged, obesity ensues.

The hypothalamus, buried deep at the base of the brain, is difficult to approach without removing or damaging many of the nervous structures above it. The stereotaxic instrument, invented in 1908 by the physiologists Victor Horsley and R. H. Clark, greatly promoted the study of the depths of the brain. It is a device which holds an animal's head rigid by a set of bars inserted in its ears and by clamps on its snout. An insulated needle can then be moved precisely in three dimensions, up-down, left-right, and forward and back, so that the uninsulated needle tip can be placed anywhere in the brain. Current passed through the needle damages tissue only around the tip, leaving the rest of the brain intact. If fixed landmarks are established— that is, the top of the brain, its midline, and the vertical plane passing through the ears—every brain structure can be mapped in terms of its distance from these landmarks. Nowadays, a stereotaxic brain atlas for many animals, like a road atlas for any country, can be obtained to guide one to stimulate, record from, or destroy any structure in the brain.

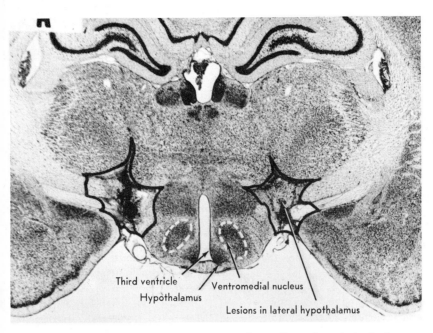

Third ventricle / Ventromedial nucleus
Hypothalamus
Lesions in lateral hypothalamus

*Figure 8-1   Photomicrograph of a transverse (frontal) section of the brain
of a rat, stained with thionin to show up cell bodies of neurons. At the base
of the brain, around the walls of the third ventricle, is the hypothalamus.
The ventromedial nuclei are clearly shown, near the third ventricle. In this
brain, there are large bilateral lesions in the lateral hypothalamic areas (out-
lined in black). Such lesions produce cessation of feeding and drinking. (P.
Teitelbaum and A. N. Epstein. Psychol. Rev., 1962, 69, 74–90, reproduced by
permission of the American Psychological Association.)*

With the aid of the stereotaxic instrument, two areas in the hypothalamus
have been found to be important in the regulation of food intake. Damage in
the ventromedial nuclei of the hypothalamus, near the walls of the third
ventricle in the midline of the brain, has been found to produce the obesity
seen in Fröhlich's syndrome. This result occurs in every animal so far investigated: man, monkey, dog, cat, rabbit, rat, mouse, and chicken. The
physiologist John Brobeck and his co-workers have shown that such animals
become obese simply because they eat too much. There is no metabolic disturbance that can explain their obesity; if fed the same amount of food on
the same schedule as a normal animal, they gain the same amount of weight;
if starved, they use their fat reserves and lose weight normally. They get fat
simply because they eat too much.

Just alongside the ventromedial nuclei, as shown in Figure 8-1, lies the
lateral hypothalamic area. Brobeck, with his colleague, Bal K. Anand, found
that precisely localized, small lateral-hypothalamic lesions produce the opposite
effect—the animal stops eating and starves to death. If both ventromedial
and lateral hypothalamic lesions are made simultaneously, the animal still
starves to death. This finding led Anand and Brobeck to conclude that the
lateral hypothalamus contains a "feeding center" whose activity is necessary

for feeding. The ventromedial area is a "satiety center" which acts as a brake to curb food intake by inhibiting the lateral excitatory feeding center. Ventromedial destruction produces a release phenomenon—the feeding center, released from ventromedial inhibition, is excessively active, with a resultant hyperphagia and obesity. More recent work, using electrical stimulation or microelectrodes to record from cells in these areas, has shown that mutual inhibition exists between the feeding and satiety centers; stimulation of the lateral hypothalamus inhibits the activity of cells in the ventromedial nuclei and vice versa.

Hypothalamic Hyperphagia

Shortly after medial hypo-thalamic lesions (see Figure 8-2), an animal eats two to three times as much as normal and gains weight rapidly. This is the dynamic phase of hypothalamic hyperphagia. Animals like the one in Figure 8-3 eventually become quite fat—doubling, tripling, or sometimes even quadrupling their normal body weight. Once they are obese, a static phase ensues, in which their weight levels off at a high plateau and each animal's food intake drops back to only slightly more than normal.

In studies of the regulation of food intake, it is customary to weigh the animal's food cup once each day. This tells us whether it has eaten a normal

Figure 8-2 Postoperative body weight and daily food intake of a typical operated animal compared to that of an unoperated normal control animal. (P. Teitelbaum. J. comp. physiol. Psychol., 1955, 48, 156–163.)

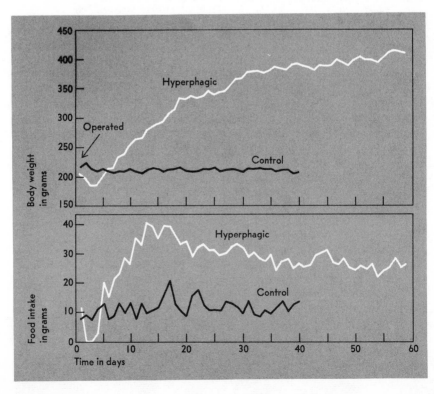

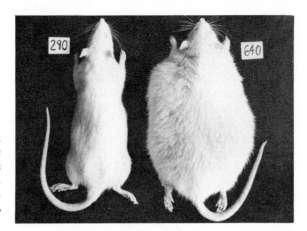

Figure 8-3 Hypothalamic obese female rat (right) compared with its normal control. (P. Teitelbaum. Proc. Amer. philosoph. Soc., 1964, 108, 464–472.)

amount, or, if hyperphagic, whether it has been overeating. But it gives no clue to how it overeats. Disturbances in feeding may exist, but the system of multiple controls that regulates daily food intake can compensate for them to achieve a constant total daily intake. For instance, consider a person who, because of ulcers or cancerous growths in the stomach, has had his entire stomach surgically removed. The cut end of his esophagus is sewn directly to the upper end of the small intestine, which is much narrower and cannot hold as much food as the stomach. Eating a normal size meal would be painful, so the gastrectomized person eats small meals, much more frequently. His meal pattern is disturbed, but his total intake is normal. By analyzing total daily food intake into separate meals, it is clear that we can often detect aberrations in feeding that would otherwise go unobserved.

How does the hyperphagic animal achieve its excess intake? We can measure the meal patterns (see Figure 8-4) by using a drinkometer, an instrument which detects and records each time the rat's tongue licks a liquid diet. A hyperphagic rat eats a normal number of meals, but each meal is twice as large. Therefore, stomach distension, one of the short-term mechanisms of satiety, does not inhibit feeding as soon as it does in the normal animal. This suggests that gastric distension acts on the ventromedial hypothalamic nuclei to inhibit feeding. Actual recording from ventromedial

Figure 8-4 Bursts of licking as recorded directly on a cumulative recorder. The pen moves up with each lick, to the right as time elapses. Each burst represents a typical meal. Left, a normal animal's meal; right, a dynamic hyperphagic animal's meal. (From P. Teitelbaum and B. A. Campbell. J. comp. physiol. Psychol., 1958, 51, 135–141.)

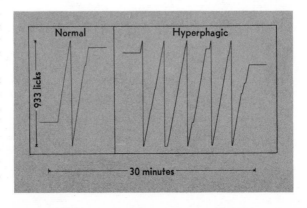

hypothalamic cells confirms this idea. Inflating a balloon in the stomach of a cat produces increased ventromedial hypothalamic activity, probably traveling from the stomach via sensory fibers of the vagus nerve. Therefore, after ventromedial hypothalamic damage, more distension is required to terminate each meal.

But total caloric regulation is also disturbed. The hyperphagic animal eats twice as much as normal. Clearly, if it eats meals that are twice as large, it could still eat only a normal amount each day, simply by eating half as frequently. One might expect an animal with a normal brain but a totally denervated stomach to eat this way. Unless it could meter its food intake by chewing and swallowing, it should have no immediate way of knowing when to stop. Therefore, it should eat larger meals, but less often, if other satiety mechanisms activated by the physiological after-effects of each meal (increased body temperature, increased utilization of sugar in the blood) were acting on its central nervous system. It would be valuable to know whether that is really what happens.

The provocative fact about a hypothalamic hyperphagic animal is that once it becomes obese, it no longer overeats. Does this mean that it has recovered from the effects of the lesion? After it is obese, we can reduce its weight to normal by starving it. Subsequently, if it has recovered from the lesion, it should be able to maintain a normal intake and weight level even when allowed to eat as much as it wishes. But in fact, it overeats all over again until it once more reaches the obese state. Therefore, some correlate of obesity must inhibit excess food intake in the fat animal. Does it do so in the normal? A normal animal will overeat if we inject it twice daily with a slow-acting form of insulin. This lowers the blood sugar for prolonged periods,

Figure 8-5   Effect of insulin injections on daily food intake and body weight. (B. G. Hoebel and P. Teitelbaum. J. comp. physiol. Psychol., *1966, 61, 189–193.)*

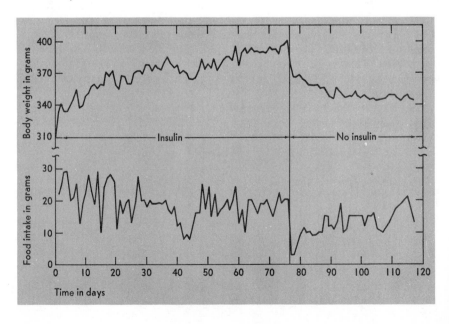

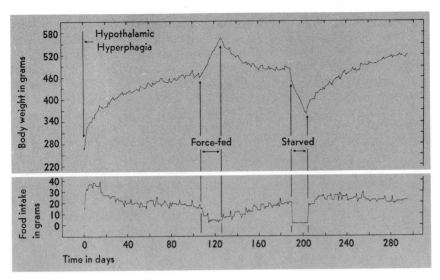

Figure 8-6 Effects of force-feeding and starvation on food intake and body weight of a rat with ventromedial hypothalamic lesions. (B. G. Hoebel and P. Teitelbaum. J. comp. physiol. Psychol., 1966, 61, 189–193.)

making the animal hungry all the time. Such a rat will become quite fat (see Figure 8-5). However, when the insulin injections are discontinued, the over-weight normal animal eats little or nothing for several days, and only begins to eat the usual amounts again when its weight has dropped to normal levels. It eats less if it is too fat.

One might say that the hyperphagic animal is like the normal; it also regulates its body weight, but at a much higher level. With fewer inhibitory cells remaining intact in the ventromedial nuclei, more obesity is required to curb intake. Perhaps this is why it overeats—because it is not fat enough. Overweight is "normal" for the hyperphagic—that is, this is the degree of obesity which inhibits his excess food intake. Like the normal, then, if the obese hyperphagic animal were made "super-obese" by overfeeding after its weight has leveled off, it should go on a diet until its weight drops to its "normal" obese level. When its weight is reduced by starvation, then like a starved normal animal, it should overeat until the "normal" weight level is reinstated. As shown in Figure 8-6, both predictions come true. Therefore, some correlate of obesity—perhaps a hormone liberated by body fat depots and carried in the blood stream—must act on the ventromedial nuclei to curb food intake. The nature of this correlate of obesity is still unknown.

THE LATERAL HYPOTHALAMIC SYNDROME

Following hypothalamic damage located lateral to the ventromedial nuclei animals stop eating and drinking. Such animals are difficult to study; in the brief time they remain alive, there is little one can do to influence their behavior as they grow steadily weaker. However, when rats with such lesions are kept alive by tube feeding, we find that they eventually recover the ability to eat and drink. Can the recovery of feeding after brain damage serve as an analytic technique to separate the multiple controls involved in normal feeding? Immediately after the lesion the animal neither eats nor drinks. Some time later it does both. Is the transition abrupt or does the animal recover in stages? Do some regulatory controls recover before others? Does the animal recover fully, or does he permanently lack abilities which the normal animal possesses? For answers, let us carefully examine the lateral hypothalamic syndrome.

Stages in Recovery

Figure 8-7 illustrates the typical effect of large lateral hypothalamic lesions on a rat's feeding and drinking behavior. (This rat was later sacrificed to study his brain. A stained section, showing the lateral hypothalamic damage, is shown in Figure 8-1). From Figure 8-7, it is clear that after such lesions recovery is very slow and takes place in stages.

Stage 1: Aphagia and Adipsia. For 19 days immediately following lateral hypothalamic lesions, the animal refused all food, wet or dry (aphagia), and did not drink any water (adipsia). It steadily lost weight until on the seventh day, it nearly died. From then on it was kept alive, by being fed through a tube passed into its stomach. Such a rat appears otherwise normal —it is typically alert, easily roused to movement, and walks readily around its cage. It ignores food, usually sitting or lying facing away from it, and actively pushes away food that is forced upon it. If such a rat sees, smells, or tastes food, or gets some on its paws or face, it engages in displacement activities, stereotyped instinctive movement patterns appropriate to instinctive acts other than feeding (hence the term displacement). For instance, the aphagic rat faced with food vigorously waves its front paws in a rapid circular motion on both sides of its face. It wipes its paws repeatedly on the floor of the cage, and if its face and mouth have food and water on them, it rubs its chin and the sides of its face on the cage floor. It does not groom itself, and allows its fur to become completely matted and caked with wet food. It can lick and swallow if a drop of milk is placed in its mouth, but soon avoids the medicine dropper and stops swallowing, allowing the milk to dribble out the side of its mouth. Ordinarily, a normal rat does not show such behavior. But it will engage in the same paw waving and wiping, chin rubbing, poor grooming, and active rejection when very bitter quinine is put in its mouth or on its paws, face, and fur. Thus, the displacement activities shown by the lateral hypothalamic rat are a sign that contact with food and water, especially mouth contact, may be highly aversive during this stage of the lateral hypothalamic syndrome. The rat behaves as if it is actively avoiding both food and water.

Stage 2: Anorexia and Adipsia. As shown in Figure 8-7, on the 20th day, although still refusing to eat dry pellets and drink water, the rat nibbled at milk chocolate and the eggnog liquid diet offered to it. It ate appreciable quantities of these wet and palatable foods, but not enough to maintain its

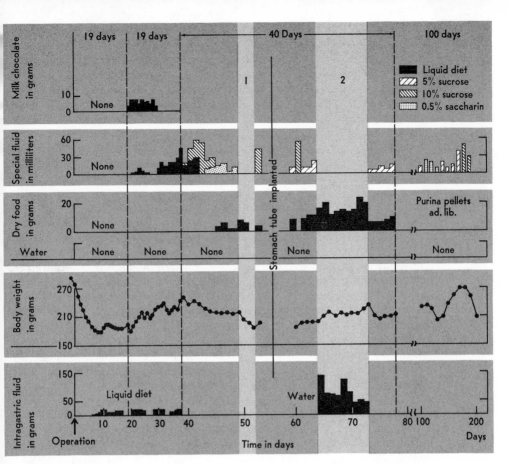

Figure 8-7 Recovery of food intake with permanent adipsia after large lateral hypothalamic lesions. The first two dashed vertical lines set off stages of recovery. First, for 19 days, the animal neither eats nor drinks; second, for 19 more days, it eats wet and palatable foods but still has to be tube-fed; and third, for the rest of its life, it regulates its food intake but does not drink water. The rat was weaned to sweet nonnutritive fluid and then ate dry food. When offered only water, shaded area 1, it did not drink and then stopped eating. Gastric hydration, shaded area 2, allowed normal feeding. Thereafter the animal ingested sweet fluid and survived on dry food. (P. Teitelbaum and A. N. Epstein. Psychol. Rev., 1962, 69, 74–90, reproduced by permission of the American Psychological Association.)

body weight, so that it still would have died if it had not been tube-fed. Though the rat was still adipsic, the aphagia had·changed to anorexia, that is, the animal ate, but not enough to keep itself alive. These changes in feeding are accompanied by many other changes in the animal's behavior towards food. It removes matted hair and dried food by licking its fur. Now when fresh, odorous, and palatable food is placed in its cage, instead of ignoring or avoiding it, the rat actively approaches and investigates it. If the food is wet, it may dip its paws in it or even take an occasional lick at it. Palatable and odorous foods are most effective in stimulating the animal to investigate and eat a little, but eating is not sustained, and displacement activities still appear. It is as though the odor, taste, and other stimulus qualities of the diet evoke feeding behavior, but there is no vigorous internal urge to eat. When a hungry normal rat is offered fresh tasty food, it gulps it down ravenously, eating rapidly and copiously. A lateral hypothalamic animal in this stage will often approach the food, pause over it, and finally eat it in a delicate and gingerly fashion even though it is quite starved. It is as though it is coaxed to eat by attractive food, not driven to it by the goading pangs of hunger.

Stage 3: Adipsia.   The anorexia ends, often abruptly. One day (the 39th day after operation for the animal whose history is shown in Figure 8-7) the rat eats a large quantity of food, and its weight takes a sudden upward spurt. It no longer needs tube feeding. Now it regulates its intake on a liquid diet (doubling its intake if the caloric content is halved by diluting it with water), and its weight returns to normal. But it is not yet fully recovered. If offered only dry food and water, the animal still refuses to drink water. Dehydration then prevents the animal from eating dry food, so that it also refuses to eat, and will die. We can prove this in two ways. Once the rat has demonstrated its ability to regulate its caloric intake on the liquid diet, we can wean it gradually to sweet nonnutritive fluids (see Figure 8-7, days 39–49). By mixing the liquid diet each day with an increasing proportion of sweet fluid, it can be weaned, first to a sucrose (sugar) solution, and from this to a saccharin (nonnutritive) solution. Thus, for the first time since the lateral hypothalamus was damaged, the rat is freely drinking nonnutritive fluid while still refusing dry food and water. As the starving rat's weight drops, it gets hungrier and hungrier until it finally (on day 47) accepts the dry, relatively unpalatable rat pellets, and maintains its weight. If the saccharin solution is then removed (as indicated in the hatched area labeled 1, starting on the 49th postoperative day), the rat still refuses to drink water, its food intake drops to zero in two or three days, it loses weight, and will die. If the sweet fluid is restored, it is accepted immediately. It eats dry food shortly thereafter, and regains its weight.

We can also use a counterexperiment (synthesis) to prove our analysis (note the hatched area labeled 2, starting on the 64th postoperative day in Figure 8-7). We again remove the sweet fluid, leaving only water and dry food. As before, the animal should refuse water and stop eating. But this time we supply water, the essential ingredient provided by the sweet fluid. Every hour, through a chronically implanted tube, we automatically pump two to three ml of water into the rat's stomach. Now hydrated normally, the animal continues to eat dry food, even though it has no sweet fluid to drink. Therefore, hydration facilitates normal feeding. Refusal to drink water produces dehydration which in turn prevents feeding. Thus, in this stage of the lateral hypothalamic syndrome, only adipsia remains, without a primary disturbance in feeding.

Stage 4: Recovery.   Some rats with very large lesions never recover further and remain adipsic, living on sweet fluid and dry food for the rest of their lives (see Figure 8-7). Eventually, however, after passing through the stages described above, most rats with lateral hypothalamic lesions begin to drink water. They continue to eat dry food, maintain their weight, and appear to have recovered. Have they regained all the regulatory controls possessed by the normal animal?

Several controls have been implicated in the regulation of food intake. Jean Mayer at Harvard University has shown that hunger is correlated with the rate at which the cells of the body utilize sugar from the bloodstream, and he speaks of a glucostatic mechanism controlling food intake. (Indeed, we have seen earlier that low blood sugar produced by insulin injections can cause overeating (see pp. 84–85).) John Brobeck points out that environmental temperature affects feeding; we eat more in the cold, less in the warm—a thermostatic mechanism. Both Mayer and Brobeck speak of cells in the hypothalamus sensitive to these changes—cells which they call gluco-receptors and thermoreceptors respectively—and much evidence points to their existence.

The lateral hypothalamic syndrome also supports their views. If we place the recovered lateral hypothalamic animal in the cold, it eats more food, just like the normal one. In a warm environment, it eats less, which is also normal. But if we lower its blood sugar with injections of insulin, then, unlike normal, it never eats more. Even if we inject so much insulin that it must overeat or die from the convulsions produced by hypoglycemia (excessively low blood sugar), it does not eat more, and succumbs. The gradual process of recovery has thus temporally separated the multiple controls ordinarily simultaneously involved in the normal regulation of food intake. Immediately after lateral hypothalamic lesions, both glucostatic and thermostatic mechanisms, and perhaps others still unknown, are impaired, and the animal eats nothing. Eventually, thermostatic regulation returns, and with it the ability to regulate caloric intake. But recovery is not complete. Glucostatic regulation is lost from the beginning and, with large enough lesions, is never recovered.

THE SIGNIFICANCE OF STAGES OF RECOVERY

There are several lessons to be learned from the lateral hypothalamic syndrome.

(1) In our search for certainty in understanding the nervous system, we often seize upon a salient symptom of damage and assign the function that is lost to a particular area. We label it and feel we understand it. We call the lateral hypothalamus a feeding center because the animal stops eating after damage there. This statement is correct as far as it goes, but further behavioral analysis of the lateral hypothalamic syndrome reveals at least two systems of tissues there, a feeding and a drinking system. New techniques further corroborate this finding. Using permanently implanted tubes as guides, cannulas with crystalline chemicals tamped into their tips can be lowered into the lateral hypothalamic areas. Nor-epinephrine (a substance that acts like adrenaline) elicits feeding in a satiated animal. In exactly the same location, carbachol (a substance that acts like acetylcholine) elicits drinking. Thus, by an independent method, we see that two anatomically overlapping systems, apparently differentially sensitive to neural transmitters, are in-

volved in feeding and drinking. Our understanding of the damaged nervous system, then, is only as good as our understanding of the behavioral disturbances which appear, so that as we improve our behavioral analysis, the functions that we attribute to the tissue grow in complexity. Who knows what other deficits are produced by these lesions? Perhaps deficits exist in many spheres of instinctive, emotional, and motivated behavior. Perhaps these animals suffer impairment in sexual behavior, in avoidance behavior, in emotional expression, or in learning capacity. We have not looked for them, so we do not worry about them. This is as it should be, because it is all too easy to become overwhelmed by fear of complexity, but we must continually guard against the inevitable comfortable oversimplifications which make us feel we understand a part of the nervous system when we have labeled it.

(2) The bizarre symptoms we see after brain damage always help us to understand normal behavior. Everything seen in the behavior of the hyperphagic or lateral hypothalamic rat can be demonstrated in the normal animal, but we usually are not aware of this until we have seen the phenomenon in the brain-damaged animal. The abnormal reveals the normal. The release phenomenon of hyperphagia acts like a magnifying glass to exaggerate the elements of normal satiety. The recovery after lateral hypothalamic damage acts like a slow-motion camera in the study of feeding. Just as slow-motion film enables us to separate out the components of a complex motor skill, like serving a tennis ball or hitting a baseball, so do the recovery processes of the nervous system help us fractionate complex behaviors into their simpler elements.

(3) Finally, we must keep in mind that the nervous system does not stand still after damage. An animal on the first day after damage may be quite different from what it will be several weeks or months later. It recovers in stages, rapidly or slowly, depending on the amount of damage and the types of tissues involved. Is there any pattern to this recovery? Is there any clue to nervous function in the way recovery progresses?

In a way, recovery of eating is like the infant's development of approach to food. Elements of feeding appear one at a time. At first, there is no voluntary approach to food or water. Only local reflexes of approach are present (licking and swallowing in response to the taste and touch of food in the mouth). Then feeding is projected into space (smell and sight of food elicits feeding), but as in the decerebrate rat or anencephalic child, caloric regulation is not present: The animal does not eat enough to maintain its weight (anorexia) and must be tube-fed to stay alive. Finally, motivational components are added; voluntary feeding manifests the urge to eat and the appearance of internal regulatory controls (thermostatic and glucostatic regulation). The parallel is striking: Very young infants, like rats with lateral hypothalamic damage, are adipsic—they refuse water, although they feed well on milk. Can it be that recovery of the nervous system parallels its development in infancy? If this is so, and it is still only a speculation, then we have an important clue to the understanding of the nervous control of behavior. We can compare infant development with adult recovery to understand the elements of normal behavior.

Regulation
and Motivation

In the study of any phenomenon, the data which make no sense are sometimes very important. They do not fit the accepted view, and are therefore ignored. Yet when they are understood, they force a revision of thought concerning that phenomenon. There are many such puzzling observations in the study of feeding.

91

Consider the hypothalamic hyperphagic rat once again. We have seen that it eats excessively, regulating its caloric intake and its body weight at a high level, often twice that of normal. But unlike the normal rat, its regulation depends critically on the palatability of its diet. We can test regulation by diluting the caloric content of food with a nonnutritive material. As described earlier, both normal and hyperphagic animals regulate their intake when eating a liquid diet diluted with water. Similarly, on a solid diet diluted with nonnutritive cellulose, normal rats increase their intake to maintain caloric regulation. Even at 75 per cent dilution, when tremendous bulk has to be eaten to get enough calories, the animals still eat appreciable amounts. In contrast, hyperphagic rats, particularly when they are obese do not increase their intake when the solid diet is mixed with cellulose. Instead of eating more, they eat little or nothing and lose a great deal of weight. A negative taste will produce the same effect. If a tiny amount of quinine is added to the diet, making it slightly bitter, for many days hyperphagic rats will refuse to eat, although normal animals ignore the taste completely. Conversely, if one sweetens the diet by mixing equal parts of sugar and food, then obese hyperphagic animals, which had stopped overeating and had leveled off in weight, overeat again and become much more obese. Again, normal animals ignore taste and ingest the same number of calories. The lateral hypothalamic animal is even more finicky. As described earlier (pages 85–89), it refuses to eat and starves to death unless offered palatable foods.

Eating is a vital homeostatic mechanism. But what kind of homeostatic control allows an animal to be so finicky? What kind of mechanism permits it to be a complete glutton if food tastes good and yet lets it die of starvation if the food tastes at all bad? Of course, in the wild, taste helps the animal

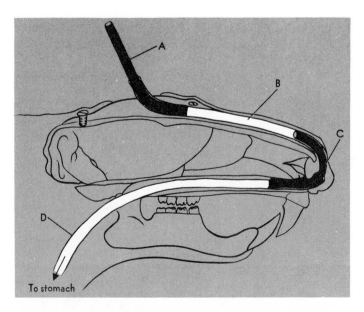

Figure 9-1 The course of the nasopharyngeal gastric tube shown in a schematic drawing of a midsagittal section of the rat's head. A and C are curved metal tubes, B and D are plastic tubes. (A. N. Epstein and P. Teitelbaum. J. comp. physiol. Psychol., 1962, 55, 753–759.)

find food and reject poisons, but why should taste be important in regulating the amount it eats? Suppose an animal could not taste its food? Would it regulate its caloric intake?

One can eliminate taste completely by cutting all three sensory cranial nerves carrying taste signals from the mouth to the brain. In the rat, however, it is extremely difficult to do so without disturbances in chewing and swallowing, and without complications resulting from the rat's inhaling food into the lungs while eating. Instead of removing taste surgically, however, one can bypass it. At the University of Pennsylvania, Alan Epstein devised a permanently implanted stomach tube for the rat, based on the nasal tube used to feed sick people in hospitals. This device is shown in Figure 9-1. A slender polyethylene tube is slipped into the rat's nostril, through the nasal passage and pharynx, into the esophagus, and down into the stomach. The outer end of the tube is passed under the skin of the snout and scalp to the top of the skull where it is anchored by screws and cement. The size of the gastric tube is exaggerated in the figure so that it can be seen clearly. It is actually so small relative to the diameter of the esophagus that the animal can eat and drink normally by mouth, even with the tube in place. Liquid food can thus be pumped directly into the animal's stomach, bypassing the receptors for taste and smell.

Figure 9-2 Schematic drawing of the apparatus for intragastric self-injection by the rat. The rat presses the bar in order to activate the pipetting machine (center) thereby delivering a liquid diet from the reservoir (left foreground) through the chronic gastric tube directly into its own stomach. (A. N. Epstein and P. Teitelbaum. J. comp. physiol. Psychol., *1962, 55, 753–759.)*

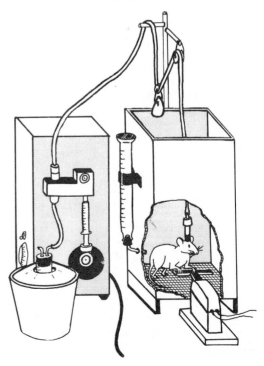

The rat is first taught to press a bar to deliver liquid food into a cup in its cage. It eats the fluid by mouth. Then the pump is connected to the animal's gastric tube, so that when the rat presses the bar, food flows directly into its stomach. A swivel device allows the animal freedom to turn without twisting the delivery tube. The arrangement is pictured in Figure 9-2. The rat can live in the cage for months at a time, feeding itself whenever it wishes, without tasting or eating the food.

As shown in Figure 9-3, a normal rat feeds perfectly well without taste. When switched from oral to intragastric feeding, it maintains normal intake and weight. It doubles its intake when the diet is diluted in equal parts with water. When the size of

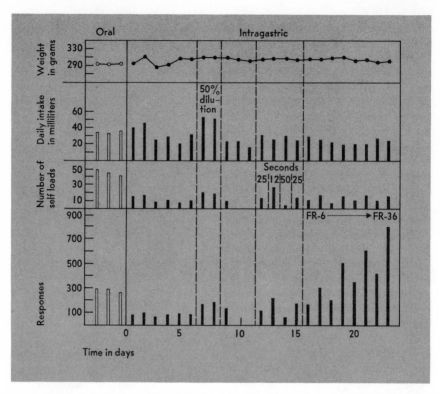

Figure 9-3 Body weight, daily food intake, the number of self-loads, and the number of daily bar-press responses during three days of oral food intake and 23 days of intragastric intake in the normal rat. (A. N. Epstein and P. Teitelbaum. J. comp. physiol. Psychol., *1962, 55, 753–759.)*

each stomach load is halved or doubled, it doubles or halves the number of loads taken. If required to press as many as 36 times for each gastric injection, it does so and ingests a normal amount.

The hyperphagic animal, on the other hand, is drastically affected by the absence of taste and smell. In Figure 9-4, we see that a dynamic hyperphagic animal (one that is gaining weight rapidly and has not yet reached an obese plateau in weight), pressing a bar six times for each delivery into its food cup of 2.5 ml of a liquid diet, eats the diet avidly. It presses the bar many times to achieve a tremendous intake of over 100 ml each day (about three times normal). When the diet is delivered directly into its stomach, however, the hyperphagic animal refuses to press the bar frequently enough to obtain sufficient food. In the absence of taste, these animals will go for many days without regulating their intake. Indeed, if the experiment had been allowed to continue long enough, some animals would very likely have starved to death.

Is taste all that is needed? Again, a proof by counterexperiment was attempted. Figure 9-4 demonstrates that merely by delivering a drop of sweet

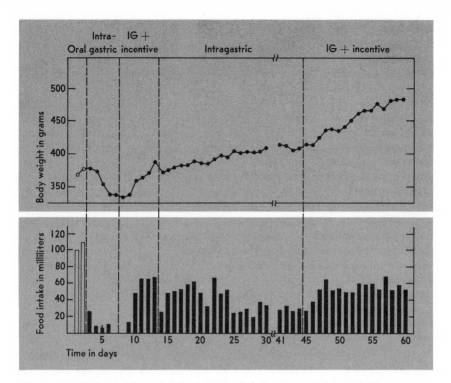

Figure 9-4 Body weight and daily food intake of a dynamic hyperphagic rat under conditions of oral intake, intragastric self-injection, and intragastric self-injection with a saccharin taste incentive. The addition of a saccharin incentive restores bar-pressing and hyperphagia (days 8 to 24), and produces a second dynamic phase and a higher level of static obesity (days 45 to 60) in a rat that was vigorously hyperphagic when eating by mouth. (D. Mc-Ginty, A. N. Epstein, and P. Teitelbaum. Animal Behaviour, *1965, 13, 413–418.)*

saccharin solution into the animal's food cup at the same time that the liquid diet is delivered intragastrically, we can transform this animal from an apathetic starving one into a vigorous hyperphagic. Indeed, after a week or so with taste, it was able to feed intragastrically without taste. But it was not very hyperphagic and its weight soon leveled off. Adding a drop of saccharin with each load once again reinstated hyperphagia and the animal became much more obese. This is exactly the way taste affects the hyperphagic when it eats by mouth, but here the effect is seen more clearly. How does taste exert such powerful control over caloric regulation?

The Concept of Caloric Regulation

To understand the currently accepted view of caloric regulation, we must trace its history. When people first began to study the behavior involved in feeding, they did not think in terms of caloric regulation. For them the problem was purely psychological:

We eat because we feel hungry and stop when we feel satisfied. Conscious sensations control feeding. The physiological basis of behavior involved in feeding was therefore naturally believed to depend on those organs responsible for the awareness of hunger and satiety.

A major change in the scientific view of the behavior that governs food intake occurred after the nineteenth century. Physiologists began to apply the experimental method to the study of living beings, and developed techniques for experimenting on animals. They had to fight to prove that the phenomena of life can be studied scientifically, and were actively opposed by the vitalists, who believed that in any living being there exists an indefinable life force, which is, by its very nature, unsusceptible to experimental analysis. The greatest step was taken by Claude Bernard, often called the father of modern physiology. He explained the mysterious ability of living systems to remain independent of many environmental changes that were known to determine the chemical and physical reactions of nonliving matter. He formulated the concept of the constancy of the internal environment (later called homeostasis): The idea that many of the body's activities serve to regulate within a narrow range the properties of the blood and other fluids that bathe all the cells of the body in the constant environment essential to their well-being, thereby making them independent of changes in the external environment. He was the first to point out that the behaviors involved in breathing, heat production and heat loss, drinking, and eating are all regulated to maintain the constancy of the internal environment.

The concept of homeostatic regulation entirely changed the physiological approach to the understanding of the behavior involved in feeding. The earlier concepts of hunger and satiety, urges to eat, and the pleasures of eating had been derived from psychological observation of people, and were of little value for the study of animals. Experiments, however, could only be performed on animals and there were no techniques available to measure the psychological aspects of their feeding. All that could be observed was their behavior; all that could be measured was the amount they ate; no other reliable estimates could be made of their hunger or of their enjoyment of food. As was pointed out by the French physiologist André Mayer, at this stage of the problem it was more useful to study feeding in terms of the regulation of food intake—the short-term variation of the amount eaten daily to adjust caloric intake in the face of changes in bodily activity, in environmental temperature, and in the energy value of food. By showing that body weight and individual tissue reserves were maintained precisely for long periods of time and were readjusted after depletion by starvation, Mayer also demonstrated the existence of long-term regulation of body weight.

The physiological question now became: How does the machinery of the body regulate food intake? A simple answer had been available for many years. In order to explain similarities between animal and human behavior without having to endow animals with souls, René Descartes, in 1664, had conceived of the reflex—that quality of the nervous system that enables the body to respond to a stimulus automatically yet appropriately, without purposiveness, consciousness, pleasure, or pain. Robert Whytt in 1763 had already demonstrated the existence of reflexes in the spinal animal. By the turn of the nineteenth century, Sir Charles Sherrington had elaborated many of their properties and had shown that they could be integrated into complex patterns of behavior at higher levels of the nervous system. As we have seen earlier, damage to the hypothalamus produces starvation, or its opposite, overeating. Anand and Brobeck pointed out that two antagonistic feeding mechanisms—a lateral, excitatory, "feeding" system held in check by a medial, inhibitory, "satiety" system—are theoretically sufficient to achieve the homeostatic regulation of food intake. Much recent evidence supports their view. For instance, lateral hypothalamic stimulation elicits feeding, whereas medial stimulation stops it. Bodily states associated with lack of food—such as increased gastric motility, decreased blood sugar utilization, and decreased brain temperature—all act to increase the activity of the lateral "feeding center." Changes associated with repletion, such as gastric distension, increased blood sugar utilization, and rise in brain temperature, cause an increase in activity of the ventromedial "satiety center" which inhibits the "feeding center" and stops the behavior involved in eating. In a very striking parallel to the control of respiration by the integration in the medulla of automatic breathing reflexes, hypothalamic integration of feeding reflexes could in principle produce the regulation of food intake. From this point of view (which is currently accepted by many physiologists), the psychological correlates of these reflexes, the urges and pleasures of hunger and satiety, are epiphenomena of the regulation of food intake; they accompany regulation but do not cause it.

Regulation and Motivation

The concept of the reflex, however, is too simple to account for the behavior involved in adult feeding. We saw earlier that infants do feed reflexively. But the reflexes of early infancy disappear, to be replaced by motivated voluntary behavior. An adult animal, even a rat, does not feed and regulate reflexively. As we have seen (p. 93), instead of eating by mouth, it can just as readily substitute an arbitrary act (such as pressing a bar for intragastric feeding) to obtain food and to regulate its caloric intake when it is hungry. In the same way, stimulation of the lateral hypothalamus does not elicit reflexive automatic eating. The psychologist Neal E. Miller demonstrated that if an animal has previously been trained to press a panel for food when it is hungry, then when stimulated electrically in the lateral hypothalamus, the animal presses the panel for pellets of food. The stimulation arouses hunger motivation and the animal uses the learned act of panel-pressing to obtain the food.

In an operant situation, when an animal uses an arbitrary act like pressing a bar to obtain food, we psychologists say that food is a reinforcing stimulus. We say that the reinforcement maintains his operant behavior, because without the reinforcement the animal fails to work. The intragastric feeding experiment described earlier showed very clearly that the taste of food is a powerful reinforcement. It maintains the operant behavior necessary to achieve caloric regulation of food intake. In the absence of taste, hyperphagic animals fail to regulate their food intake. With taste, they eat avidly. Clearly, the reinforcement provided by food lacking in taste is not sufficient to maintain the behavior involved in eating. Food provides the immediate reinforcement of taste, and in addition, that of stomach distension. We have seen earlier that a hyperphagic eats much larger than normal meals, suggesting that a greater-than-normal stomach distension is necessary for satiety. Without taste, and with a less sensitive stomach, the immediate reinforcement provided by food is not sufficient to maintain operant behavior, and caloric regulation is thereby lost also. One might expect a normal animal to fail in caloric regulation, if each intragastric injection were made very much smaller. This is exactly what happens.

There are, then, at least two kinds of homeostatic regulatory mechanisms: reflexes and behavioral regulations. Reflexes, such as those involved in control of heart rate, blood pressure, and respiration, go on automatically, without awareness, whether the animal is unconscious or awake. Some, like those involved in infant feeding, grasping, and avoiding, usually require wakefulness; but each one is still a built-in fixed response to a particular kind of stimulus. Behavioral regulations have developed even further. Motivated voluntary acts achieve the necessary regulation. Feeding, drinking, and many aspects of temperature regulation are such behavioral regulations. They are motivated acts and are governed by the same variables that control operant behavior. This explains why taste is so important when caloric regulation is impaired. Taste is a powerful reinforcement that maintains the motivated behavior involved in feeding. It is a psychic energizer that increases the urge to eat. The pleasure provided by the taste of food is necessary for caloric regulation. Whenever a voluntary act is being used (and this applies to all adult mammalian feeding), there can be no regulation without motivation.

The great power of the physiological approach to behavior lies in the method of analysis: Simplify in order to understand. But in its great strength lies a dangerous pitfall—oversimplification. This is clearly seen in our study of the regulation of food intake. In an attempt to be parsimonious, many neurophysiologists have restricted their view of the nervous control of feeding to the concept of automatic reflex regulations, and have relegated motivated behavior to the behavioral variables and neurophysiological mechanisms that control food-getting. But only when we understand motivation will we understand feeding.

THE ROLE OF THE HYPOTHALAMUS
IN MOTIVATED BEHAVIOR

The hypothalamus integrates several kinds of instinctive and regulatory behavior patterns. Different areas apparently serve different functions. We have seen that electrical stimulation in the lateral hypothalamus elicits feeding in satiated animals. Stimulation of the hypothalamus in the region in front of and medial to the lateral feeding centers elicits drinking in goats and rats. Minute amounts of hypertonic salt water solutions injected in this area stimulate goats to drink as much as nine liters of water at one time, to the point of extreme gastric distension. This evidence suggests that "osmoreceptors" (cells in the hypothalamic drinking areas sensitive to osmotic pressure) control thirst. Nearby, in the preoptic area of the hypothalamus, mechanisms for temperature regulation are found. Cooling the preoptic area elicits shivering and constriction of skin blood vessels in goats and dogs. Heating this region elicits panting and vasodilation. When a microelectrode is used to record the activity of single neurons, we find that some cells in the preoptic area are directly activated by local heating, while others are excited by local cooling. These hypothalamic cells are therefore receptors for temperature change— that is, "thermoreceptors."

Hormones can also stimulate the hypothalamus. Estrogen pellets implanted in the anterior hypothalamus of rats or the posterior hypothalamus of cats produce full-blown sexual behavior in ovariectomized animals which otherwise display no sexual receptivity. Minute quantities of testosterone injected into the preoptic hypothalamus of a male rat yields an astonishing sight— the male shows vigorous maternal behavior: It retrieves young pups and returns them to the nest just as a nursing mother rat would do. This experiment shows that at least some of the brain structures controlling both male and female behavior are present in every animal, but are inactive unless stimulated by hormones. (Why testosterone, the male sex hormone, should produce female maternal behavior is not yet understood.)

These hypothalamic tissues must, then, be sensitive to sex hormones. Quantities so small as to be ineffective if injected systemically produce vigorous instinctive behavior when deposited directly into the hypothalamus. From Bard's experiments, years earlier (see pp. 55–56), it was clear that such hormonally sensitive tissue in the hypothalamus must exist; with improved techniques of localization, they have been demonstrated.

It is also clear from Bard's experiments that the hypothalamus is necessary to integrate instinctive, emotional, and regulatory behavior patterns into effective sequences. When the hypothalamus is separated from the midbrain, medulla, and spinal cord, isolated fragments of feeding, sexual, or emotional behavior appear, but never their integrated expression. How does the hypothalamus accomplish such integration?

We have seen earlier that it has been customary to speak of hypothalamic integration of reflexes. Thus, spinal reflex patterns of crouching, tail deflection, and treading come under hormonal control when the hypothalamus is connected to the nervous system below. But we have also seen that the behavior patterns evoked by hypothalamic stimulation in the intact brain are not reflexive. Lateral hypothalamic stimulation arouses the urge to eat, not the reflex automatisms involved in feeding. To obtain food, the stimulated animal will press a bar or cross an electrically charged grid. Goats stimulated in the "drinking" center perform the learned instrumental act of climbing a staircase to obtain water. The same is true of temperature regulation: Evelyn Satinoff, at the University of Pennsylvania, trained rats to press a bar for heat when they were in a cold environment (see Figure 9-5). In the hypothalamus of each rat, she then implanted a very small thermode (a tube bent in a U-shape) so that the preoptic area could be cooled by running a very cold fluid through the thermode. She found that rats, just like dogs and goats, shiver when the hypothalamus is cooled. But, in addition, if they had previously been trained to press a bar for heat in the cold, then, when the hypothalamus was cooled, they pressed the bar to get bursts of infrared heat. Even in a neutral environmental temperature in which they needed no heat, and would, therefore, ordinarily not work for it, they did so when their brains were cooled. Unless they were responding to their reflexive shivering

Figure 9-5 The heat-reinforcement apparatus. In a cold environment, the rat depresses a lever that activates the heat lamp. (B. Weiss and V. G. Laties. Science, *1961, 133, 1338–1344.)*

(which is unlikely), they must have been aware of the feeling of cold in the brain because they used a learned operant response to counteract it. Therefore, in addition to eliciting the reflex response of shivering, cooling the hypothalamus produces the sensation of cold and the motivation to keep warm.

These operant techniques introduce a new dimension into the study of brain and behavior. We used to study reflexes in anesthetized animals and in isolated portions of the nervous system, such as the spinal cord; now we study instinctive and learned behavior in awake animals. We used to speak of the integrative action of the nervous system mainly in terms of the integration of automatic reflexes; now we speak of the integration of complex instinctive and voluntary activities. The hypothalamus is still thought to integrate homeostatic systems, but we must now speak of hunger and the urge to eat when we describe the regulation of food intake.

The hypothalamus integrates the series of instinctive acts from appetitive to consummatory behavior. It may do so by producing the appropriate motivational state. In other words, the hypothalamus may be necessary for the existence of a motivational state which welds together appetitive and consummatory behavior into integrated instinctive activities. Therefore, when damage to the hypothalamus impairs instinctive activities such as eating, drinking, or mating, the impairment may not necessarily result from primary damage to the structures responsible for the individual components of these acts (such as chewing, swallowing, or mounting). Rather, the impairment may result from damage to the motivational processes that must energize the components sufficiently so that they can be elicited by the normally effective stimuli. If this hypothesis is correct, then, increasing the level of motivation, either by using supernormal stimuli or by changing the internal environment, may be sufficient to elicit the behavior once again, although under normal circumstances it would appear to be permanently abolished.

Emotion

Reinforcement is the technical term used to indicate the satisfaction provided by an operant act—the pleasure experienced when we perform an act, obtain an object, or produce a desired outcome. How does one feel pleasure? How, indeed, does one feel any emotion?

In a classic approach to levels of nervous function, Philip Bard, in a manner exactly similar to his analysis of sexual behavior, examined the nervous integration of emotion. By sectioning the nervous system of the cat at various levels, Bard showed that the hypothalamus must be connected to the lower parts of the nervous system for the integrated expression of emotion to occur. Bard studied rage behavior, an emotional pattern clearly apparent in the normal cat. The Hallowe'en black cat presents a typical picture of full-blown rage: Hissing, growling, spitting, and screaming, the enraged cat stands prepared to attack or flee with back arched, eyes blazing (pupils dilated), hair standing on end, claws unsheathed, heart racing, and blood pressure high—a classic example of coordinated, sympathetic nervous system activity. If sufficiently enraged, a normal alley cat will spring to the attack, able to kill or seriously injure an animal, even animals much larger than itself. The decorticate cat is more easily moved to rage than the normal; the slightest pinch of its tail or leg provokes rage of high intensity. But, in a cat without a cortex, the attack lacks direction; pinch the tail and the enraged decorticate will strike, hiss, and claw, but at the ground in front of it, not at the pinching stimulus. As soon as the pain ends, the rage subsides; one can quickly place one's hand into the decorticate animal's mouth without fear; the rage lacks the normal after-discharge which enables it to persist in the absence of external stimuli. For these two reasons, decorticate rage is called "sham rage"; it is the integrated expression of rage without the awareness and persistence characteristic of normal emotion. Sham rage is easily released in the absence of the cortex (very slight stimuli evoke it); therefore, cortical processes must normally inhibit the expression of rage. Removal of all forebrain above the hypothalamus also produces sham rage. If a section is made behind the hypothalamus, however, separating it from the nervous system below, then coordinated rage cannot occur. The decerebrate cat shows fragments of emotional expression—such as growling, purring, hissing—but they are no longer integrated properly into the full pattern. For instance, the decerebrate cat will often show signs of contentment (purring) while hissing and growling in rage. Therefore, the hypothalamus is necessary for the integration and coordination of emotional expression.

Papez' Circuit: The Nervous Substrate of Emotional Affective Experience

In order for an animal to experience emotion, certain structures in the forebrain must be intact. The clue to the system of structures involved in the experience of emotion was furnished in 1937 by the neuroanatomist James W. Papez.

Papez was impressed by the symptoms produced by the rabies virus, a syndrome terrifyingly displayed in the mad rabid dog. Characterized by intense emotional, convulsive, and paralytic symptoms, rabies seemed to offer a clue to the neural structures involved in emotion. In human beings, as the disease

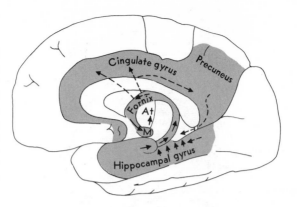

Figure 10-1 The shaded area of cortex represents what was formerly known as the limbic lobe of Broca, and· later, the rhinencephalon. M, mammillary body; At, anterior thalamic nucleus. (P. D. MacLean. Psychosom. Med., 1949, 11, 338–353.)

sets in, insomnia, irritability, and restlessness are seen; these usher in a stage of excitement and profound emotional disturbance. There is extreme hyper-irritability to all kinds of stimuli, such as light and sound, and every stimulus situation provokes great apprehensiveness and paroxysms of fear. The patient presents the appearance of intense fright and of mingled terror and rage. Hydrophobia, or fear of water, develops, possibly as a result of painful pharyngeal spasms when the patient attempts to swallow fluids. Foaming at the mouth is a common symptom of autonomic disturbance.

Lesions in the nervous system are produced by rabies, often in the hippocampus and hypothalamus, both of which structures are part of the middle wall of the brain (see Figure 10-1). From a careful study of the evolution of the brain, Papez came to the conclusion that the medial wall of the cerebral hemisphere is connected anatomically and physiologically with the hypothalamus, and that the lateral wall is related to the dorsal thalamus. Papez reasoned that the sensory pathways from the receptor organs split into three routes at the thalamic level, each conducting an important stream of impulses. One route conducts impulses through the dorsal thalamus to forebrain structures believed to be involved in motor activities. This route represents the "stream of movement." The second conducts impulses from the dorsal thalamus to the lateral cerebral cortex. This route represents the "stream of thought." At the same time, the third pathway conducts a stream of impulses to the hypothalamus. Since the hypothalamus is involved in emotional activities, this route represents the "stream of feeling." Therefore, the structures in the midline wall of the cerebral hemispheres, related to the hypothalamus, should be involved in the experience of emotions.

The hippocampus (see Figures 10-1 and 10-2), through a fiber bundle known as the fornix, sends impulses through the septal area to the mammillary bodies, nuclei in the posterior hypothalamus. These impulses are then sent along the mammillothalamic tract to the anterior nuclei of the thalamus and are relayed by them to the cingulate cortex. Thus, from cortex (hippocampus) to hypothalamus and back to cortex (cingulate gyrus), a circuit is formed enabling thought to affect emotional expression and vice versa. More recently, the amygdala, a structure lying near the hippocampus and related to the hypothalamus by a fiber bundle, the stria terminalis, has also been

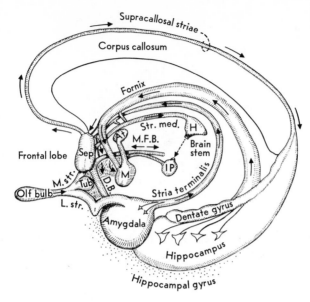

Figure 10-2 Schematic representation of relationship of main subcortical structures and connections of rhinencephalon, drawn as though all of them could be seen from the medial aspect of the right hemisphere. For diagrammatic purposes some connections have been given an arbitrary course. Abbreviations: At, anterior thalamic nucleus; D.B., diagonal band of Broca; H, habenula (part of epithalamus); IP, interpeduncular nucleus; L. str., lateral olfactory stria; M, mammillary body (part of posterior hypothalamus); M.F.B., medial forebrain bundle; M. str., medial olfactory stria; Olf Bulb, olfactory bulb; Sep, region of septal nuclei; Str. med., stria medullaris; Tub, olfactory tubercle (head of caudate below). (After Krieg, from P. D. MacLean. Psychosom. Med., 1949, 11, 338–353.)

included in these midline structures, which are collectively known as the rhinencephalon (smell brain), and also as the limbic system.

ANALYSIS OF THE LIMBIC SYSTEM

A great deal of study has been devoted to the limbic system since Papez' paper in 1937, and his speculations have received several striking confirmations.

The Septal Syndrome

On their way from the hippocampus to the hypothalamus, the fibers of the fornix pass through, are joined by, and give off connections to a mass of cells clustered together in a region of the forebrain known as the septal area. In 1953, psychologist Joseph V. Brady, and neuroanatomist Walle H. Nauta teamed up at Walter Reed Hospital to study the neural substrate of emotional behavior. They discovered that lesions in the septal area of rats (Figure 10-3) produce a set of symptoms which, in some respects, strikingly resemble some of the signs of rabies.

After septal damage, ordinarily placid rats become strikingly alert with eyes intently following the movements of the observer approaching the cage. Explosive startle reaction is produced by a slight puff of air on the skin of the back (hyperirritability?) or by presentation of almost any auditory stimulus.

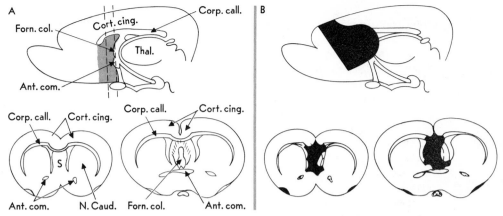

Figure 10-3 (A) *Semidiagrammatic representation of the rat forebrain. Upper figure: midline view of the right half of the brain with septal region gray. Lower figures: two frontal sections at levels indicated by dashed lines through gray area of upper figure. Ant. com., anterior commissure; Corp. call., corpus callosum; Cort. cing., cingulate cortex; Forn. col., fornix columns; N. caud., caudate nucleus; Thal., thalamus.* (B) *Medial and frontal reconstructions of a septal lesion in the brain of a rat. Such lesions produce hyperemotionality. (J. V. Brady and W. J. H. Nauta.* J. comp. physiol. Psychol., *1953, 46, 339–346, and 1955, 48, 412–420.)*

The typical exploratory response of the normal rat to a harmless object such as a pencil is replaced in the septal-damaged rat by "freezing" (normal rats generally "freeze" when they are frightened) with the whiskers turned stiffly forward. Rapidly approaching objects are attacked immediately with vicious biting. If one attempts to capture or handle the animal it responds by fierce attack or vigorous flight. Often, merely opening the cage door will provoke the animal to leap right out. When five or six such septal animals are placed together in a cage, they will all stand rigidly alert on their hind legs, watching each other. The slightest move by any of them, or any slight noise can trigger an explosive chain reaction of screaming, leaping, and biting attack.

Structures Involved in Drinking

As described earlier (pp. 89–90), cholinergic (acetylcholine-like) stimulation in the lateral hypothalamus elicits vigorous drinking. More widespread exploration of the brain has recently revealed that drinking can be produced by cholinergic stimulation of structures all along Papez' circuit, that is, from hippocampus through septal area and lateral hypothalamus. Since hydrophobia is a prominent symptom of rabies, one might well have predicted such a finding.

The Neural Basis of Pleasure

One of the most exciting discoveries in recent work on the nervous system was made in 1954 by the psychologists James Olds and Peter Milner, working together at McGill University. They had started out by trying to determine whether electrical stimulation in various parts of the reticular activating system in the brain of rats would enhance the rat's ability to learn a maze. However, in some parts of the brain, particularly in the septal area, electrical stimulation had an apparently deleterious effect on maze-learning. Instead of running correctly and rapidly through the maze to get to the food in the goal box, the rats, when stimulated electrically, stopped running and wandered back the way they had come. Strangely enough, they seemed to be going back to the place in the maze where they had received the brain stimulation, acting as though they were searching for it. Why should they seek brain stimulation? Could it be that they actually liked it? Would they be willing to work for it? From the work of Olds and others, it is now well-known that many species (among them rats, cats, dogs, monkeys, and even dolphins) will press a bar thousands of times per hour, hour after hour, to obtain electrical stimulation of the brain. People stimulated in similar subcortical regions report pleasure. Rats, even when very hungry, cross an electrified grid more willingly for brain stimulation than for food. They will work on pay-off schedules for brain stimulation, as they do for other reinforcers such as food and water. Neutral stimuli, such as a light or a tone, when paired with appropriate brain stimulation, acquire secondary reinforcing properties (the rat now works to receive only the light or tone). Therefore, brain stimulation, in the right places, is reinforcing. As Olds and his co-workers have shown, and again, as Papez might have predicted, many of the brain structures in which stimulation is reinforcing lie in the rhinencephalon, along the course of a fiber tract known as the medial forebrain bundle. As shown in Figure 10-4, this runs upstream and downstream between the olfactory bulbs, the lateral hypothalamus, and the midbrain, making connections with, and receiving fibers from, many of the limbic structures that it passes along the way.

We can also see in Figure 10-4 that more medial stimulation is aversive. As discovered originally by psychologist Neal E. Miller and his colleagues at Yale University, animals will learn a response to escape stimulation in the medial periventricular system that runs through the ventromedial areas of the hypothalamus into the midbrain. Taken together, these two systems, one positive and one negative, provide a physiological substrate for pleasant and aversive emotional experience.

VOLUNTARY APPROACH AND AVOIDANCE

What does it mean to say that brain stimulation is positively reinforcing? Subjectively, the stimulus must feel good—we enjoy it and want more. Objectively, when dealing with others than ourselves or with animals, we use the second half of our definition to verify the first half: If the subject wants more, he enjoys it. If, when he is given control of the stimulus, he voluntarily and repeatedly causes it to occur, we know he wants and therefore enjoys it. But how can an animal want a stimulus he has never experienced before? The initial pleasure must arouse a desire for more. Memory of the act which produced the reinforcing stimulus must create the anticipation that it will do so again. With desire and anticipation aroused, the animal performs the act and receives the stimulus.

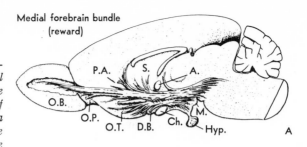

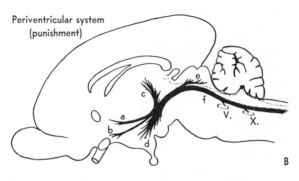

Figure 10-4 (A) Diagram representing medial forebrain bundle (the presumed substrate of reward mechanism) in a generalized and primitive mammalian brain. Some abbreviations are: A, anterior commissure; D.B., nucleus of the diagonal band; M, mammillary body; S, septum. (B) Similar diagram representing the periventricular system of fibers (presumed substrate of punishment mechanism). Some abbreviations are: b, anterior hypothalamus; c, thalamus; d, posterior hypothalamus; e, tectum. (After Le Gros Clark, from L. Stein. Ciba Found. Symp. on Animal Behaviour and Drug Action, *ed. by H. Steinberg. London: J. & A. Churchill, Ltd., 1964, 91–113.)*

Why do we have to deal with such vague concepts as pleasure, desire, memory, and anticipation? We know that reflexes are simple built-in neural mechanisms for approach and avoidance of stimuli. Why not say that a stimulus of sufficient strength automatically elicits reflex movements of approach or avoidance? Why not explain self-stimulation in the brain as a simple approach reflex? The brain stimulus elicits approach which triggers the stimulus again and again. The accidental pressing of the bar produces the stimulus. This elicits reflexive approach to the bar, and again accidentally triggers the stimulus, which causes the entire cycle to repeat. It is all automatic: The animal does not know it is going to receive the stimulus, nor does it desire it.

Does the stimulus control the animal's behavior (automatic) or does the animal's behavior control the stimulus (voluntary)? Is the act a reflex or an operant? As we have seen earlier (pp. 56–59), the nature of the act is critical. If it is unlearned, stereotyped (invariable in form), and is only a consequence of the stimulus, it is a reflex. But if the animal can be taught to use any arbitrary act or sequence of acts to obtain the stimulus or if the animal will actively seek the stimulus and adjust his actions to obtain it (as in maze-running), we can be absolutely certain it is not automatic; it is an operant act, subject to the control of motivational states and past learned experience. Exactly the same reasoning applies to the medial system where stimulation leads to operant behavior which avoids further stimulation.

Therefore, these systems in the brain are involved in voluntary approach and avoidance.

How are these systems related to the more automatic unlearned mechanisms of approach and avoidance? Does stimulation of the positive reinforcement system facilitate reflexes of approach such as sucking or grasping? What relation do these systems have to instinctive approach (controlled by internal hormonal states as well as external stimuli)? In this respect, it is interesting that lateral hypothalamic stimulation, which elicits approach to and ingestion of food, is also positively reinforcing; that is, the animal will press a bar repeatedly to produce the brain stimulation that ordinarily induces him to eat. Why should the animal thus work to make himself hungry? Isn't hunger unpleasant? Or are some forms of hunger (appetite) enjoyable?

If the positive reinforcement system facilitates approach, how does it affect avoidance? Perhaps the two systems (approach and avoidance) are mutually inhibitory. Does destruction of one of them "release" the other from inhibition? We know that medial hypothalamic activity inhibits feeding. Destruction of the ventromedial hypothalamic nuclei leads to hyperphagia, presumably through a release of the lateral hypothalamic feeding system. It should also release lateral hypothalamic self-stimulation. Bartley Hoebel and I have recently shown that it does, supporting the idea that the negative (avoidance) system inhibits the positive (approach) system.

We know that infantile reflexes of approach and withdrawal disappear as voluntary behavior develops. Do the systems for voluntary approach and avoidance develop at the same time? Might they be essential to the development of voluntary behavior? Would destruction of the positive system retard development of voluntary approach, and conversely, would stimulation accelerate it? Clearly there are more questions than answers in this area of physiological psychology. But they are important questions, and hopefully, will soon be answered.

Cortical Control
Mechanisms

The reflexes of infancy disappear as the child grows older. Complex patterns of behavior develop, in which voluntary control often predominates. Although it is still poorly understood, the development of voluntary behavior appears to parallel the postnatal development of the brain, particularly the cerebral cortex. What happens to an adult when areas of the cortex are removed? Does he become more infantile? Consider a person suffering from damage to the frontal lobes.

109

It is often very difficult to detect frontal-lobe damage. There is no obvious loss of function—no paralysis of the limbs, no anesthesia or loss of sensory discrimination on the skin, no gross impairment of intellectual function, memory, or emotional capacity. Because the frontal lobes are very highly developed in man, and because this development distinguishes his brain from that of lower animals, many people have tried to prove that complex intellectual processes, such as intelligence, memory, insight, and so on, depend on the presence of the frontal lobes. But for every investigator who believes he has found such a deficit, there is another who finds no difference between normal people and those with frontal-lobe damage.

Still, behavioral differences do exist after frontal damage. I was very much impressed by this when I attended Dr. Derek Denny-Brown's lectures on neurology at Harvard medical school. When he discussed the frontal lobes, Denny-Brown conducted a neurological examination of a patient suffering such damage. He put the patient at ease, asked him how he felt, and asked his permission to examine him while the young doctors were present. He tested his reflexes, the knee and ankle jerk in response to a tap on the patella (knee), or Achilles' (ankle) tendon with a blunt plastic hammer. He tested his ability to detect a light touch with a cotton ball on the skin surfaces of arms, legs, and body. He did the same for pressure with a pencil eraser, and for pain by lightly pricking his skin with a pin in various places. He tested his hearing by asking him to close his eyes and to localize the position of a pocket watch as he moved it around the patient's head at various distances from his ears. He tested his memory: "What day is this?" "What did you eat for lunch?"

In the course of the examination, while asking the subject various things, Denny-Brown, standing beside and slightly behind the patient, while both were facing the class, lightly touched the side of the patient's cheek, near the mouth. A curious thing occurred. The side of the patient's mouth near the stimulating finger opened and gaped toward the finger. As the stimulation continued, the patient's head turned, his mouth made contact with the finger, and sucking movements occurred. If such a patient is asked why he is doing this, he may show surprise and embarrassment, replying that he was not aware of his action, or even denying it, yet he may be unable to stop. These are involuntary automatisms, rooting and sucking reflexes, no longer subject to voluntary control by the patient with frontal-lobe damage.

Similar approach automatisms can be demonstrated in the hand and foot. Involuntary grasping of the hand is often a diagnostic sign of frontal-lobe damage in human beings (Figure 11-1). The best way to elicit it is to distract the patient's attention by asking him to look at something on the side wall of the room, or to perform some simple task of mental arithmetic with his eyes closed. While he is thus engaged, the palm of his hand is lightly touched and gently stroked by the examiner's index finger in a movement from

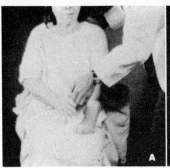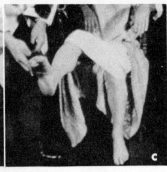

Figure 11-1 (A and B) *Involuntary grasping and pursuit of the retreating stimulus in the right hand in a patient with left frontal tumor.* (C) *The toe grasp in the foot.* (D. Denny-Brown. J. nerv. ment. Dis., 1958, 126, 9–32, copyright © 1958, The Williams and Wilkins Co., Baltimore, Md.)

the center of the patient's palm outward between the thumb and forefinger. Depending on the amount of damage to the frontal lobes, and also on how much paralysis has been caused by damage simultaneously occurring in the motor areas of the brain, various components of the grasping reflex can be elicited. Deep pressure in the palm elicits strong maintained flexion of the fingers (grasping). Light touch in a stroking movement of the skin elicits closure of the fingers around the stimulating object (trap reaction) in such a way as to prevent it from leaving the palm. Rhythmic flexion and extension of the fingers (forced groping) then occur in a manner which acts to bring the object back to the center of the palm where it can be firmly grasped. If the object is moved out of the palm, the hand and arm follow after it (pursuit reaction), and if the object is moved just slowly enough, the hand and arm follow while just clinging to it (magnet reaction). The same kind of grasping can be seen in the foot in response to pressure or a light touch on the sole.

These actions are very powerful and often not subject to voluntary control. They pervade the frontal-brain-damaged patient's behavior, often to his great embarrassment. Thus, when opening a door, the patient may find himself unable to let go of the doorknob. The grasp reflex is so powerful, that he has to reach over with his other hand and pry his fingers loose. In bed, when he sees a nurse passing by, his hand may automatically reach out and clutch at her dress, an act particularly distressing if she happens to be carrying a tray loaded with food or medicine. The contact approach-reflex of the foot is often so exaggerated that, when walking, the frontal-damage patient is often hampered by the slipping-clutch syndrome: When he starts to walk, his feet seem glued to the ground and he has to make several sliding movements on the ground before he can finally free his feet enough to walk forward normally.

Thus, the approach reflexes of mouth, hand, and foot, which disappear during infant development, reappear in the adult after damage to the frontal lobes. One may speculate then that in the course of normal development, the frontal lobes exert an inhibitory influence over these reflexes which, in some manner, integrates them into voluntary behavior.

It is interesting to note that recovery of voluntary control after frontal-lobe damage, like recovery of feeding (see p. 90), parallels its development in infancy. The same progression occurs in both—from control only by local contact reflexes (forced grasping in response to deep pressure) to control by more tenuous and distant stimuli with projection into space (forced grasping, magnet reaction, and visual control over grasping) to eventual voluntary control of reaching and grasping.

PARIETAL-LOBE DAMAGE:
RELEASE OF WITHDRAWAL REFLEXES

Damage to the parietal areas of the cortex, just posterior to the sensori-motor cortex, produces a syndrome which in many ways is just the opposite of the frontal-lobe syndrome. Instead of exaggeration of approach, there is exaggeration of withdrawal. Touching the side of the patient's cheek produces firm closure of the mouth and a turning away of the head. Touching or stroking the palm produces extension and spreading of the fingers. If the stimulation is strong, the whole arm will flex and the hand will be withdrawn. In some cases, this withdrawal reflex is projected into space. Thus, as shown in Figure 11-2, even the sight of an approaching doctor will often cause a parietal-lobe patient's hand to rise involuntarily with fingers spread and extended until the hand cuts off the sight of the approaching doctor. The behavior strongly resembles the exaggerated fright and withdrawal posture of a superstitious person trying to ward off the evil eye.

Touching the sole of the foot produces the Babinski reflex, a diagnostic sign of damage in the sensori-motor-parietal area. The reflex consists of

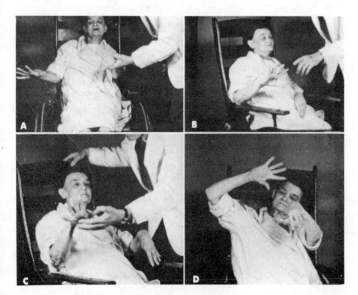

Figure 11-2 The patient, aged 59, with a history of left hemiplegia with parietal signs, suddenly developed right-sided parietal lobe signs one week before the photographs were taken. The upper photographs (A and B) show the "spontaneous" posture of levitation of the right arm that occurred as the examiner approached the patient, increased as the examiner's hand entered the right visual field, and (C) greatly increased by stroking the palm of the right hand. (D) The limbs remained for many minutes in any posture passively applied to them. (D. Denny-Brown and R. A. Chambers. Res. Pub. Assoc. Res. nerv. ment. Dis., 1958, 36, 35–117.)

spreading extension of the toes and upward flexion of the ankle, often combined into a mass withdrawal reflex of the entire limb. The gait of a parietal patient is often peculiarly like that of a peacock—the upward movements of lifting the leg off the ground are very brisk and excessively high; that is, an exaggeration of leg withdrawal from ground contact.

Visual contact-approach reflexes are inhibited by reflexes of withdrawal. Like a normal cat or dog, a normal child held in the air over a table reaches toward the table top when he sees it (see Figure 11-3). This is visual placing. However, after parietal damage, the child will show exaggerated visual withdrawal; it cannot stand or walk on any surface because its limbs fold up and collapse when it sees or is brought into contact with such a surface.

Unilateral damage (to one side of the brain) will produce these forms of behavior on the opposite side of the body. Thus, a patient with damage to the right parietal lobe will show exaggerated withdrawal reflexes of left hand and foot. He can use his right hand for voluntary action, but the left is paralyzed, that is, unavailable for voluntary action. He is anesthetic on the left side, unable to feel stimuli on the skin of the arm or leg. When he dresses himself, he dresses the right half of his body, slipping his right arm and leg into jacket and pants, but completely ignoring the left half; he does not dress his left arm or leg and does not notice them at all. If it is pointed out to him, he will often deny that he is not fully dressed. This affliction has often been called disturbance of the body image—the patient acts as though he has forgotten or can no longer conceive his body image appropriately. But, as Denny-Brown points out, we may also understand this behavior as an exaggeration of withdrawal reflexes in response to stimuli on that side of the body. The patient withdraws from all stimuli on that side—those in space as well as those from his body—to such an extent that he completely ignores or suppresses all stimulation from that side. He withdraws from stimuli so well that he doesn't see them, feel them, think about them, or remember them.

This theory is still speculative and should not be taken as a proven explanation of the forms of behavior resulting from parietal or frontal damage. It may be a tremendous oversimplification to try to encompass all manifestations of these disturbances as exaggerated reflexes of approach or withdrawal. And yet, these simple ideas make sense out of a great many phenomena

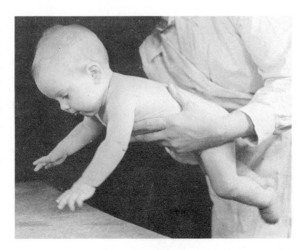

Figure 11-3 Visual placing of the arms in a 257-day-old girl. When lowered toward a supporting surface, the infant stretches her arms out even before touching the surface. (A. Peiper. Cerebral Function in Infancy and Childhood. New York: Consultants Bureau, 1963, p. 195.)

which go together, and which would otherwise seem unrelated. Rooting, sucking, and grasping do serve to approach and contact a stimulus. All are exaggerated after frontal damage. Withdrawal of mouth, hand, and foot from noxious stimuli do reappear in exaggerated form after parietal damage.

Whatever the final interpretation may be, it is clear that any destruction of the nervous system always produces two kinds of loss of function: (1) loss of excitatory function—as in paralysis after damage to cells responsible for movements, or anesthesia after damage to cells involved in sensation; and (2) release phenomena—exaggerations of behavior resulting from the loss of cells that exercise an inhibitory control over excitatory systems in the brain. Thus, as an infant develops, inhibitory systems somehow exert control over the basic reflexes of approach and withdrawal. Presumably, the frontal lobes inhibit reflexes of approach, and thereby subject them to voluntary control. The parietal areas must inhibit reflexes of withdrawal. When these areas are damaged, the voluntary controls are destroyed and the primitive mechanisms are once again released. The concept of release from inhibition was most clearly expressed by the brilliant English neurologist John Hughlings Jackson. In 1884 he wrote:

The higher nervous arrangements, which have developed from the lower complexes, keep the latter in check just as a government which has its origin in the people supervises and guides the people. The "dissolution" [of function in the central nervous system] is not only a "taking away" of the higher accomplishments, but at the same time a "release" of the lower centers. If the governmental body of this country were to be suddenly dissolved, two causes for complaint would arise: the loss of the service of outstanding persons and the anarchy of the now unsupervised people. The loss of the governmental body corresponds to the breakdown in our patients, and the anarchy to the now no longer supervised activity of the next lower stage of reduction.

Epilogue   In the introduction to this book, I pointed out that certain ways of trying to understand behavior are basic to physiological psychology. Accepted "facts" are continuously re-evaluated in the light of new evidence based on improved techniques, but the fundamental ways of seeking understanding remain the same. To emphasize this, I quote from the closing paragraphs of a little book, written with an aim similar to mine in 1824 by Pierre Flourens.

1. Now, if we think about it even slightly, we will soon see that all the facts I have gathered here, are *simple facts; simple facts* that it was necessary to disentangle from the complicated ones in which they are enmeshed.

2. In physiology, when we make a mistake, it is almost always because we have not adequately seen all the complexity of the facts.

3. Because, basically, everything in the mechanism of life, both the phenomena and the organs, is complicated.

It is necessary, therefore, to break down phenomena, that is to say, to isolate them from all diverse circumstances; it is necessary to dissect organs, that is to say, to distinguish all their distinct parts.

In a word, it is necessary to arrive at simple facts.

4. The art of isolating simple facts is the whole art of experiment.

Selected Readings

Chapter 1

Bernard, C. *Introduction to the study of experimental medicine.* New York: Dover, 1957.

Descartes, R. Rules for the direction of the mind. In *Philosophical works of Descartes.* New York: Dover, 1955. Vol. 1, 1–77.

Chapter 2

Békésy, G. v. Current status of theories of hearing. *Science,* 1956, Vol. 123, 779–783.

——. Similarities between hearing and skin sensations. *Psychol. Rev.,* 1959, Vol. 66, 1–22.

——. Some electromechanical properties of the organ of Corti. *Annals of Otology, Rhinology and Laryngology,* 1954, Vol. 63, 448–468.

Ratliff, F. *Mach bands: quantitative studies on neural networks in the retina.* San Francisco: Holden-Day, 1965. Chaps. 2–4.

Chapter 3

de Robertis, E. *Histophysiology of synapses and neurosecretion.* Oxford: Pergamon Press, 1964. Chaps. 1–3.

Hodgkin, A.L. *The conduction of the nerve impulse.* Springfield: C.C. Thomas, 1964.

Chapter 4

Fechner, G. *Elements of psychophysics.* New York: Holt, Rinehart and Winston, 1966.

Stevens, S.S. To honor Fechner and repeal his law. *Science,* 1961, Vol. 133, 80–86.

Chapter 5

Pavlov, I.P., *Conditioned reflexes.* New York: Dover, 1960.

Sherrington, C.S. *The integrative action of the nervous system.* New Haven: Yale University Press, 1906. (Issued as a Yale Paperbound, 1961.)

Skinner, B.F. *The behavior of organisms; an experimental analysis*. New York: Appleton-Century-Crofts, 1938.

Tinbergen, N. *The study of instinct*. New York: Oxford University Press, 1951.

Chapter 6

Peiper, A. *Cerebral function in infancy and childhood*. New York: Consultant's Bureau, 1963.

Chapter 7

Jouvet, M. Neurophysiology of the states of sleep. *Physiol. Rev.*, 1967, Vol. 47, 117–177.

Kleitman, N. *Sleep and wakefulness*. Chicago: University of Chicago Press, 1963.

Luce, G.G. and J. Segal. *Sleep*. New York: Lancer, 1967. Entire book.

Chapter 8

Code, C.F. (ed.), *et al. Handbook of physiology*, Section 6, Alimentary canal. Washington: American Physiological Society. Chapters on the regulation of food and water intake.

Chapter 9

Teitelbaum, P. The use of operant methods in the assessment and control of motivational states. In W.K. Honig (ed.). *Operant behavior: areas of research and application*. New York: Appleton-Century-Crofts, 1966, 565–608.

Chapter 10

Heath, R.G. *The role of pleasure in behavior*. New York: Harper and Row, 1964. Articles by Olds, Stein, Lindsley, and Hernández-Peón.

Papez, J.W. A proposed mechanism of emotion. *A.M.A. Arch. neurol. Psychiat.*, 1937, Vol. 38, 726–743.

Chapter 11

Denny-Brown, D. The nature of apraxia. *J. nerv. ment. Dis.*, 1958, Vol. 126, 9–32.

———— and R.A. Chambers. The parietal lobe and behavior. *Res. Publ. Ass. nerv. ment. Dis.*, 1958, 36, 35–117.

Index